The Bug Lover's Song Book

camilla cancantata

Introduction

The Bug Lover's Songbook is an attempt to re-frame the world as some non-human species might perceive it - especially those creatures with whom our relationship is often troubled or uncertain. I have used the word bug in its non-scientific context, to refer to invertebrate animals (ie without a spine) that are generally small, including insects but also slugs, spiders, woodlice etc.

Inevitably there is a degree of anthropomorphism; often an animal is the narrator of the song, rather than being sung about. I have tried to translate what I think the animal might say if we were to engage in an honest conversation about co-existence between species on earth, when the human is not accorded special status but is just another example of evolution, regardless of size of brain or development of tool use. Humans have, to my mind, developed a false sense of entitlement to the richness of life; we behave as if we own the earth rather than being temporary inhabitants. Sometimes the songs are just about the animal and how it lives its life, because humans are largely irrelevant to it. What is it like, for example, to be constantly aware of the threat of predation?

As far as possible the details of life cycle, habits, and evolution are accurate according to current knowledge. But every day scientists uncover new facts, discover new species or wonder at new aspects of behaviour.

Because the text is important, and needs to be understood, the music is generally simple, without complex rhythms or harmonies. I have written piano accompaniments similar to those I might play myself, but also given basic harmonies so that anyone who wants to perform the songs can make up their own accompaniment using the same or similar chords. Likewise feel free to transpose the songs if other keys are more convenient; the most important thing is to make the words clear. The recordings are mostly faithful to the written notes, with the occasional variation.

The songs are meant to entertain as well as inform – and to be fun to sing and play – I hope you enjoy them.

Contents

Insecta

3   A Weevil isn't Evil
15   Earwigs
27   Caterpillar Munching
37   The Sad Wasp
47   Diptera!
56   Plight of the Arctic Mosquito
64   Chocolate (the midge that pollinates it)
73   Can you find me? (grasshopper)
80   Praise the Beetles
90   Queen Bumble
105   Good Connections

Myriapoda

115   How Many Legs? (centipedes and millipedes)

Armadillidae

123   Woodlouse

Arachnida

132   Spiders, Spiders

Clitellata

140   Earthworms

Gastropoda

147   I'm a Snail
157   Soliloquy of the Slug

Finale

171   Life is all around us

A Weevil isn't Evil

Weevils are from an ancient lineage. They belong to the order Coleoptera, or beetles, who were well established by the Jurassic era, when flowering plants first appeared on the earth.

Weevils are generally quite small, compared to other beetles, and are currently classified in two groups - 'true' and 'primitive'. The Curcolionidae or True Weevil family contains thousands of species.

As the song mentions, weevils occupy very specific narrow niches; they might feed off just one part of a particular tree. And of course early weevils evolved in an age long before humans, when there were no tasty cultivated crops around for them to eat.

Most animals are opportunistic, when it comes to food...you take what you can find. Humans being no exception – remember how many animals we have hunted to extinction.

A Weevil isn't Evil

Chorus:
A weevil isn't evil, it does what weevils do
And if you know your weevils you can learn to love them too
Humans weren't around when weevils first evolved
We, not weevils, are the problem to be solved!

V1
A weevil isn't evil, but it likes to share our food
And if it gets inside the plants the outlook isn't good
Coffee, avocado, and all sorts of grain
Are lovely food for weevil grubs, and that is a pain – but

Chorus

V2
The hungry youngsters eat a lot – it's all they have to do
And that means damaged crops, and loss of money too – but
Growing different plants together makes it hard to choose
And then those little weevils will get a bit confused

Chorus

V3
A weevil's legs are short and thin, it can't walk very far
If its forest home's destroyed, it can't jump into a car
So if you're planning on a clear-cut, stop and have a think
About the millions of tiny creatures you will make extinct

Chorus

V4
A weevil isn't evil, it does what weevils do
As well as being food for birds and frogs and hedgehogs too
On a thriving planet full of life all can take their share
So let the weevils have their space – they won't be everywhere!

Chorus

A Weevil isn't Evil

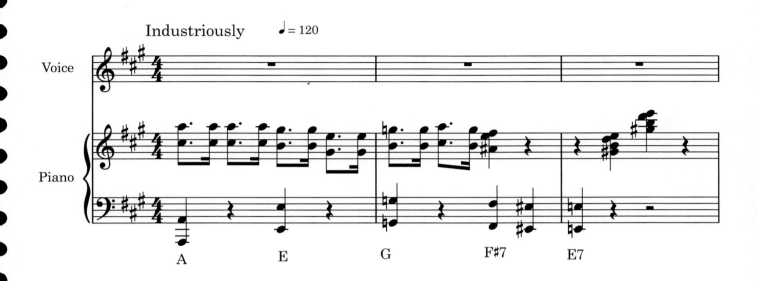

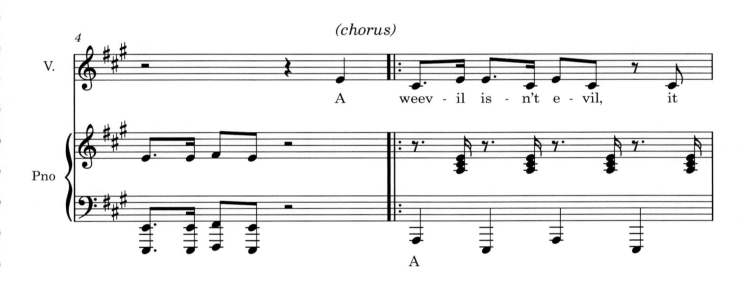

A Weevil isn't Evil

learn to love them too Hu - mans weren't a - round when

weev - ils first e - volved We, not weev - ils, are the

(end chorus) *(verse 1)*

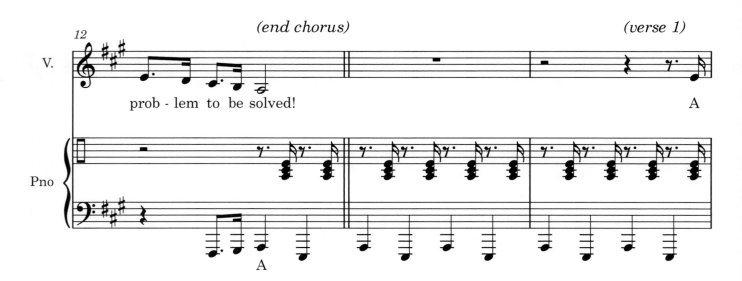

prob - lem to be solved!

A Weevil isn't Evil

A Weevil isn't Evil

A Weevil isn't Evil

A Weevil isn't Evil

(verse 3)

A Weevil isn't Evil

A Weevil isn't Evil

A Weevil isn't Evil

(final chorus)

won't be ever - y where! A weev - il is - n't e - vil, it

does what weev - ils do, And if you know your weev - ils you can

learn to love them too Hu - mans weren't a - round when

A Weevil isn't Evil

weev - ils first e - volved   We, not weev - ils, are the prob - lem to besolved!

Earwigs belong to the order Dermaptera, meaning 'skin wings', but in fact although they have functional wings, they rarely bother to use them. They are easily distinguishable by their slender bodies and relatively large back pincers – which are mainly used for defence.

For some reason there used to be a theory – totally unfounded – that earwigs would crawl into a person's ear and from there, burrow into the brain and lay eggs. Whether the name came before the story or the other way round is not known.

The common European earwig Forficula Auricularia enjoys munching up woolly aphids which can infest apple trees. It will also predate other creatures that can get in the way of a good harvest, such as codling moth, so it's an all-round useful animal to have in apple and pear orchards.

Despite increasing research proving the devastating effects of insecticides, especially the infamous neonicotinoids/neonics, profit-hungry corporations are still pushing these products which are destroying insects in vast numbers, especially bees, and the ecosystems of which they are part. There are now increasing concerns about the effects of neonics and other pesticides on human health.

When we truly understand the complexities of insect predation, we can find ways to grow food successfully without using toxic insecticides.

Earwigs

V1
Let me make it very clear, I don't want to live in your ear
I just want to be happy in the apple tree
And though I might nibble on a little bit of petal
You just need to see what a good friend I can be!

Chorus:
Earwigs, earwigs, we just want to be
Happy in the apple tree

V2
We find aphids very tasty, so don't you be too hasty
With poisonous spray – that's really not the way
You can't kill off one pest without destroying all the rest
Of us insects living peacefully

Chorus

V3
If you find us back to back nestled into a crack
Don't assume immediately that we're harming the tree.
We like a cosy nest where we can snuggle with the rest
Of our friends and family

Chorus

V4
We look after our young with tender care -
Unlike aphids, we only have one brood a year
And once they're grown up they need to get away
'Cos Mamma might eat the ones that stay!

Chorus

V5
So if your hand reaches out for a can of toxic spray
Remember all the aphids we can munch up in a day
Their numbers may recover from insecticide
But us poor earwigs will all have died!

Chorus (x2)

Earwigs

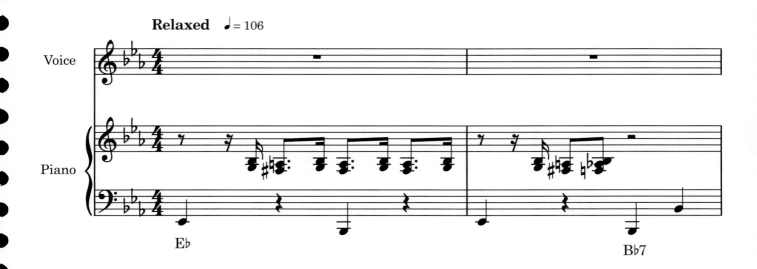

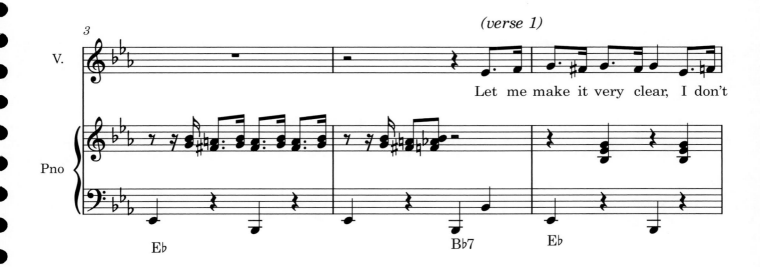

Earwigs

Earwigs

(verse 2)

We find a - phids ver - y tast - y, so

don't you be too hast - y with pois - on - ous spray

That's real - ly not the way___ You

Earwigs

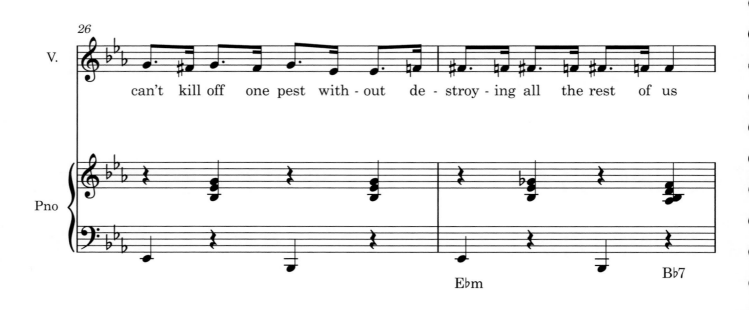

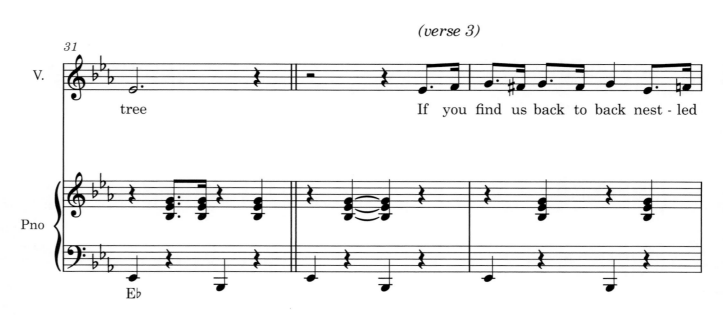

Earwigs

Earwigs

Earwigs

Earwigs

Earwigs

Earwigs

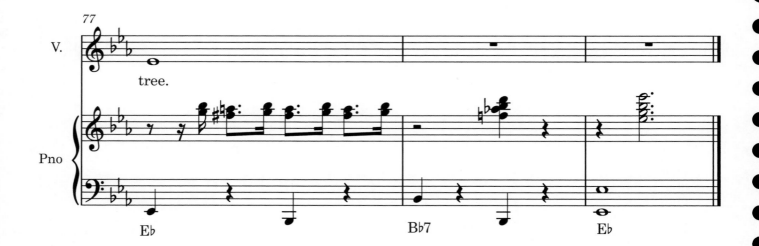

Caterpillar Munching

'There is nothing in a caterpillar that tells you it's going to be a butterfly' (R. Buckminster Fuller).

A caterpillar starts off so small, its only mission is to eat and eat so it has enough protein to metamorphose/transform, from voracious munching caterpillar to motionless pupa and eventually into a butterfly or moth.

As the caterpillar increases in size, its outer skin or exoskeleton gets too tight – so it sheds it to reveal a soft one underneath. Then it does something really clever – breathes out to put plenty of space between the current body and the new soft skin so there's room to expand. Then the new skin hardens.

The average caterpillar moults four or five times and the stages between moults are called instars. Each instar has more prickles or confusing colours or tastes worse than the previous one.

It's a perilous life – eating your surroundings while trying to avoid being eaten yourself!

Caterpillar Munching

V1
Caterpillar munching, caterpillar crunching
Decimating the vegetation
Eating machine, tearing through green
Leaves without hesitation

Chorus:
Watch out, there's predators about
Time is short – don't want to get caught

V2
We have devised ways to survive
We can blend in with stripes on our skin
Lots of fine prickles will give birds the tickles
We're not that tasty, but rather nasty

Chorus

V3
Got to keep growing, can't be slowing
Down our daily rate of chewing
This is only the start of things
Wait to see what the future brings

Chorus

V4
Five times we shed our skin
Before we start to spin a
Silk cocoon, in which to hide
While everything breaks down inside

Chorus

V5
Outside we seem so still
Inside great changes will be happening
Until one day
We emerge and fly away

Chorus

V6
Fly butterfly, fly away
Stretching your wings on a sunny day
Fly butterfly, don't you wait
Around too long to find a mate

Fly butterfly, fly away
Stretching your wings on a sunny day
Lay your eggs, and soon there'll be
More caterpillars munching,
Caterpillars munching,
Munching, munching
Happily

Chorus x2

Caterpillar Munching

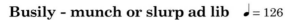

(verse 1)

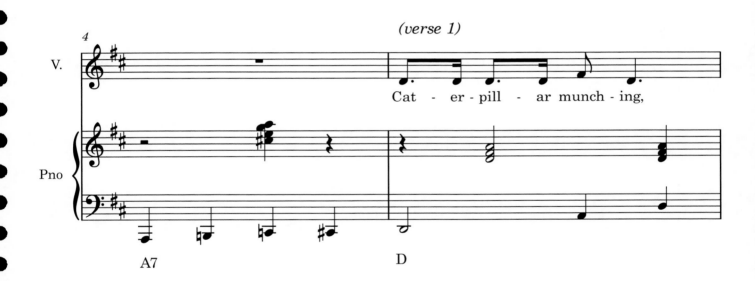

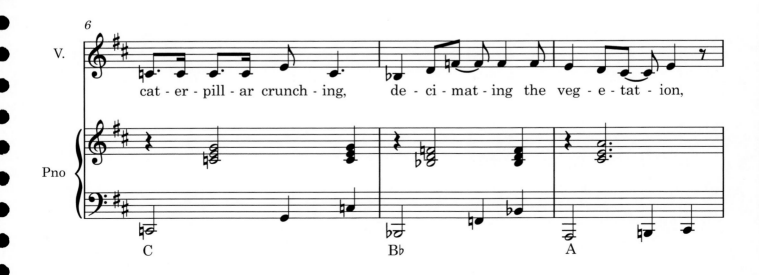

Caterpillar Munching

Caterpillar Munching

Caterpillar Munching

Caterpillar Munching

Caterpillar Munching

Caterpillar Munching

Caterpillar Munching

The Sad Wasp

Wasps precede bees, evolutionarily speaking – bees are vegetarian versions of wasps, and evolved with flowering plants.

This song is about a worker wasp from a colony – the so-called 'eusocial' wasps (there are solitary wasps too but their lives are different). The colony has a queen, workers, and drones. The queen wasp mates in the summer, then hibernates over winter and starts a new colony the following spring. The first eggs she lays are female worker wasps.

For most of their lives, these sterile female wasps work really hard, expanding the nest structure, foraging for food and looking after their baby siblings. The babies reward them with a sugary secretion that keeps them going with their hectic life style. But in late summer, the queen slows down and finally stops laying eggs, and eventually the workers have no more grubs to feed and tend, which means they don't get the sugary food either.

And then what? Work has evaporated and food supplies are low and the poor wasps are hungry and longing for sugar. That's when they come buzzing around human homes and gardens looking for a fix – some rotting fruit or jam or anything else sweet and energising.

Be kind to them – these are the same wasps that have been pollinating your plants and munching up unwanted visitors on your vegetables such as aphids or caterpillars. Life has no meaning for them any longer and their home has collapsed. They will not survive once the weather gets colder so cheer them up and let them eat some jam.

The Sad Wasp

V1

You may see a bee, but a bee is not me,
I'm a wasp, I be a wasp
I have a bad reputation for causing havoc in the kitchen
And general consternation
When there's sugar around, or jam to be found
But that's only because I'm a wasp that is lost,
And seeking some sweetness at the end of my days
Want to go out in a jam-filled haze

Chorus:

I'm a wasp that is lost, have pity on me
Though I sting, I'm a wasp, not a bee!

V2

I worked all year to serve my Queen
And now there's no job left for me.
It's all falling apart, the home's a mess
I'm drunk and disorderly.
I can't work out where to go in life
So I hover around your jammy knife

Chorus

V3

So hide the sugar, and cover the jam
And don't pay attention to me
I'll fly away on drooping wings
In thirst and misery
On some rotting fruit I will end my days
Buzzing around, all sugar-crazed

Chorus

I'm a wasp that is lost, have pity on me
Though I sting, I'm a wasp not a bee!

The Sad Wasp

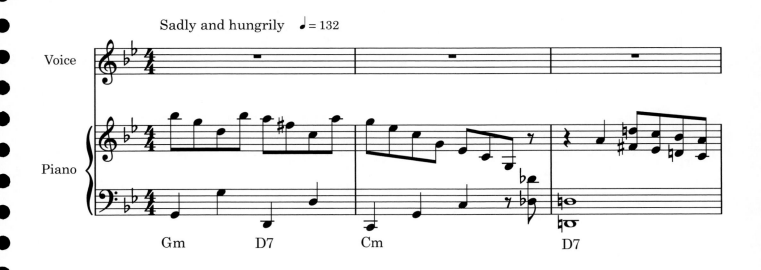

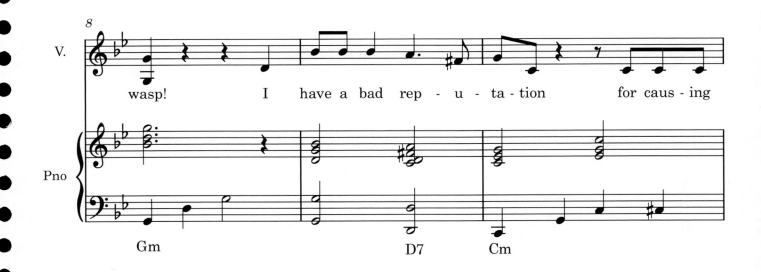

The Sad Wasp

The Sad Wasp

The Sad Wasp

(verse 2)

I worked all year to serve my queen, and now there's no job left for me It's all fall-ing a-part, the

The Sad Wasp

home's a   mess,   I'm   drunk and dis - ord - er - ly   I

can't work our where to   go in   life, so I hov - er   a - round your

(chorus)

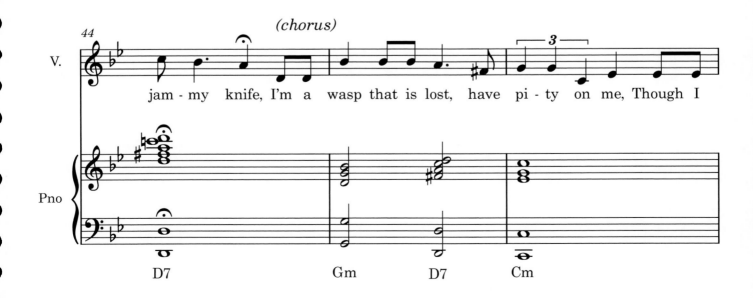

jam - my   knife, I'm a   wasp that is lost,   have pi - ty   on me, Though I

The Sad Wasp

The Sad Wasp

me   I'll   fly   a - way   on droop - ing wings, in thirst and mi - ser -

Gm   D7   Cm   D7

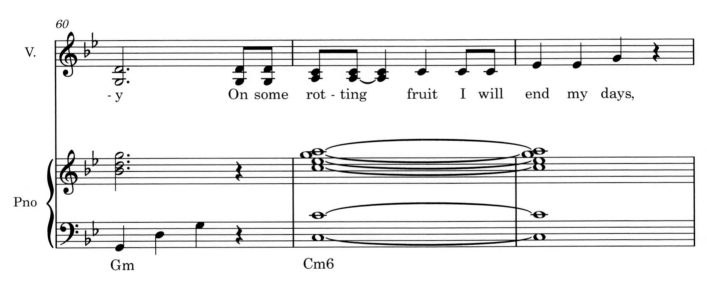

- y   On some rot - ting   fruit   I   will   end   my   days,

Gm   Cm6

(chorus)

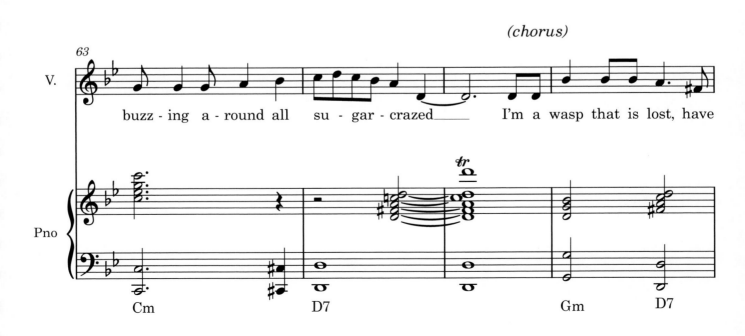

buzz - ing a - round all   su - gar - crazed____   I'm a wasp that is lost, have

Cm   D7   Gm   D7

The Sad Wasp

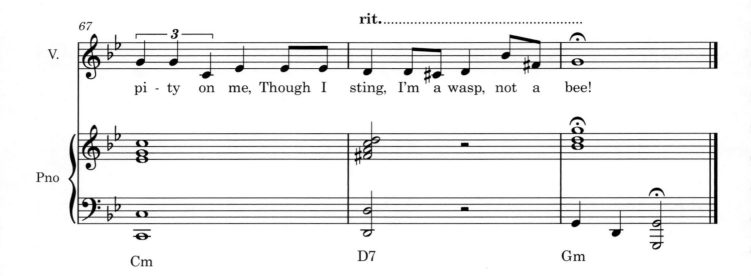

pi - ty on me, Though I sting, I'm a wasp, not a bee!

Cm   D7   Gm

Diptera!

Diptera is the Latin for 'two-winged', (di = two, ptera = wing) which, along with a pair of halteres, tiny balancing knobs in place of back wings, characterises the true flies. Not all creatures called flies are actually flies: scorpion, stone, caddis and snake flies all have two pairs of wings and so do not belong in Diptera. A few (mostly parasitic) Dipterans have evolved to be completely wingless. They all go through a larval stage and then pupate before emerging as adult flies.

Most flies lay eggs, but a few fly families, such as the calyptrates, have by-passed egg-laying entirely; the eggs hatch inside the mother and are fed inside her by a special gland, before emerging as baby larvae. This is useful if your food supply is going to decompose fast – the larvae can start feeding straight away without hanging around in egg form.

The earliest fossil records of flies date from about 260 million years ago, and most modern fly families had evolved by about 34 million years ago. In the UK alone there are at least 7,000 different species of fly, ranging from elegant crane-flies to hover-flies that look like bees, to horse-flies and familiar house-flies. World-wide there must be millions of species, many of them as yet unknown to scientists.

Flies have a really hard time living with humans. Yet they have so many roles in ecosystems. They are tremendous pollinators and are less susceptible to disease than honey bees – that's not a reason to stop protecting honey bees but all pollinators are vitally important. Flies can also survive extreme temperatures and there are species of flies living in both the Arctic and Antarctic. Some larvae have evolved to live in very hot petroleum pools, and others in salt water. With their adaptability, flies will probably cope with climate change better than many other animals – it is predicted that as the planet heats up, the world population of house flies could expand by over 200% in a few decades.

Flies - like many other less loved insects - recycle enormous quantities of waste matter. It's the young maggots who do the eating, which is why the adults lay their eggs where they do. Ok so seeing flies buzzing around dead bodies or piles of excrement may be unpleasant – but life would be a lot more unpleasant if they didn't. But because they can be on a dung heap one minute, and then in someone's kitchen the next, (a house-fly can travel up to 10 miles at a speed of 5 miles an hour) human-fly relationships can get complicated. They can also taste with their feet with special taste receptors, which is why you may see them wandering thoughtfully across your food.

Flies have amazing vision and see in all directions. Their compound eyes process about 250 images a second, whereas humans only process around 60 images a second. This means that to a fly, we move in slow motion, so they can easily dodge swatting and blustering humans as they do aerial acrobatics around us.

The larvae tend to live much longer than the adults, who may only survive a day or so – just in time to mate and lay their eggs. And in their turn the adult flies are often food for bigger animals, that have evolved to see as fast as them – think of swallows swooping over the surface of a river snapping up flies and midges.

Flies are essential to the healthy functioning of ecosystems, they keep the earth clean, and are adaptable and resilient and beautiful - they deserve our respect!

Diptera!

Chorus:
Dip dip dip diptera, two two two winged we are
Flies, flies of every size – dip dip dip diptera!   (x2)

V1
Terrible hairy, flat-footed, robber or soldier
Could be down a drain or in a leaf on a tree
Recycling, transforming, disinfecting, pollinating
Keeping the earth clean and free

Chorus

V2
Fungivores, detritivores, coprophages, necrophages
Sucking up the waste that would drown the earth
Parasitic, predatory, flesh-eating or veggie
Part of the great cycle of death and rebirth

Chorus

V3
Murderous, courageous, formidable, voracious
Happy in the tropics, or Arctic ice
Stalk-eyed and gorgeous, miners and borers
Mosquitoes, biting gnats and flies with hairy eyes

Chorus

V4
Love them or hate them, stop to admire them
Explorers, survivors, cleaners sublime
Filth eaters, blood suckers, could be living inside fungus
Praise to the flies who evolved over time

Chorus x 2

Diptera!

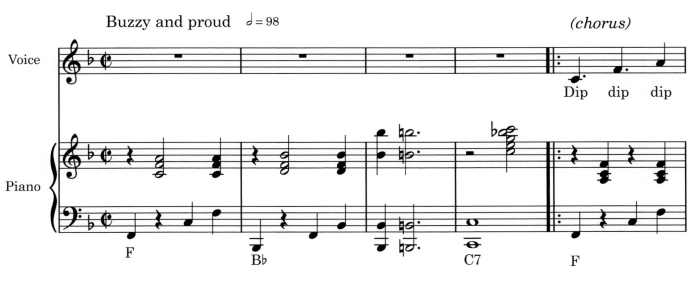

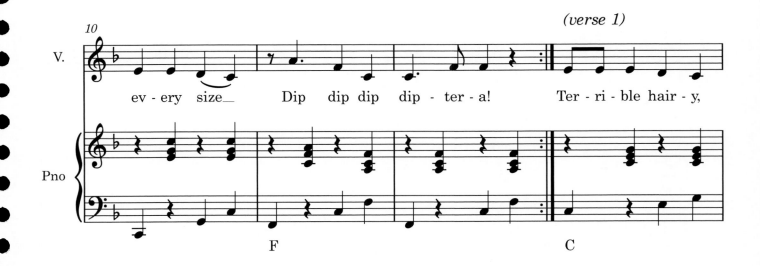

Diptera!

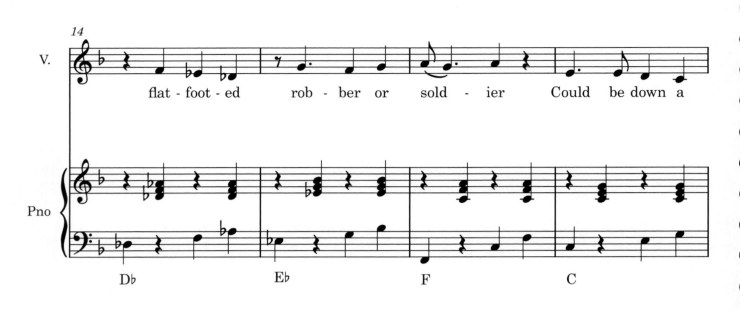

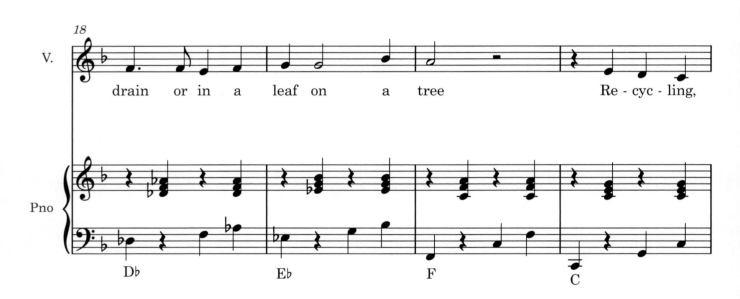

Diptera!

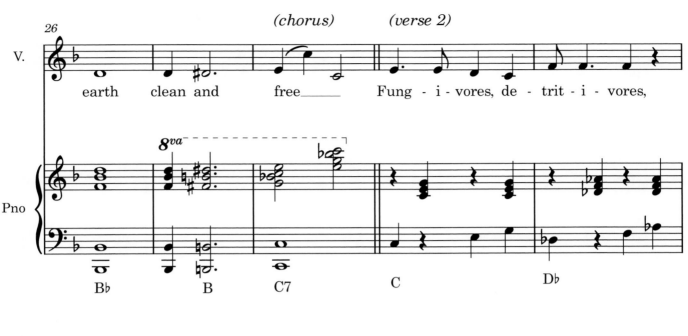

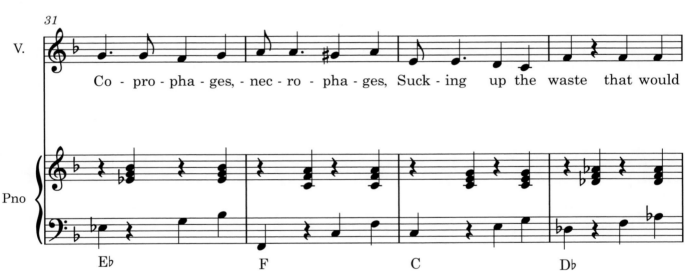

Diptera!

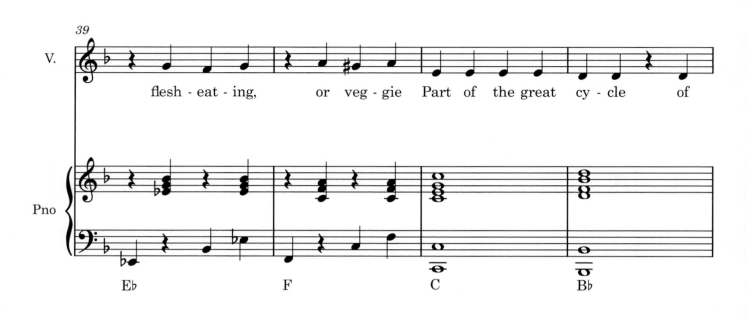

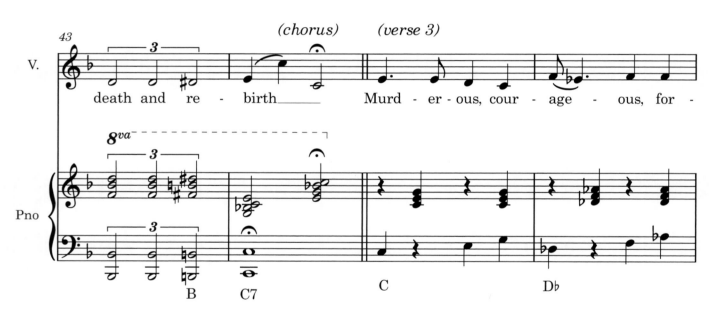

Diptera!

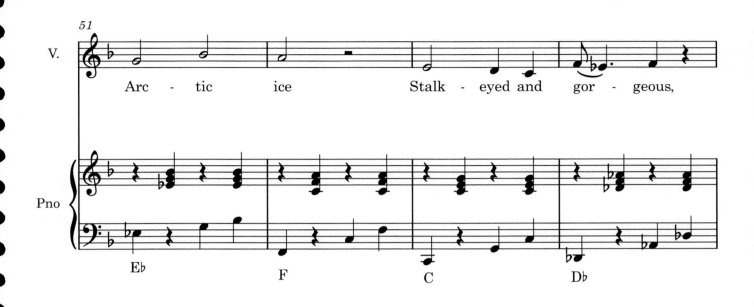

Arc - tic ice Stalk - eyed and gor - geous,

mi - ners and bor - ers Mos - qui - toes bi - ting gnats and

(chorus) *(verse 4)*

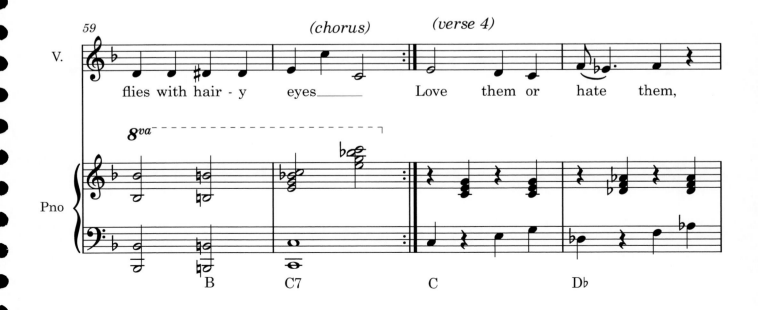

flies with hair - y eyes_____ Love them or hate them,

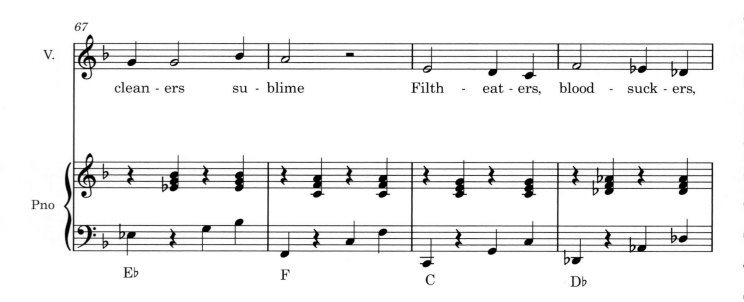

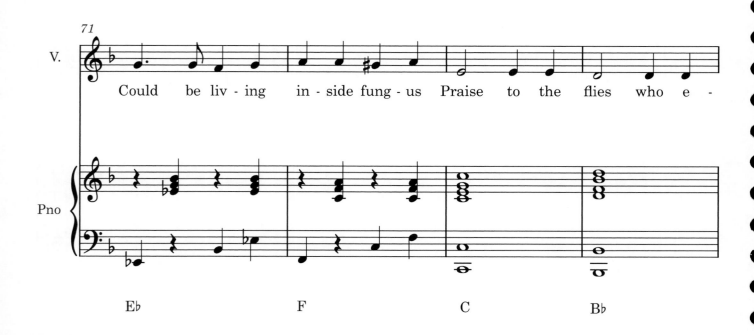

Diptera!

Plight of the Arctic Mosquito

This mosquito is contemplating a melting iceberg.

The song is inspired by a paragraph in the book A Naturalist's Guide to the Arctic, by Evelyn Crystalla 'EC' Pielou, a Canadian mathematical ecologist. Describing the life of the female Arctic mosquito, she writes: 'consider the hardships they face'.

The female mosquito needs just one blood meal to lay her eggs - just like the cocoa midge. But she has to fly a long way to find a convenient mammal in the Arctic. So tiny, in such harsh conditions, and yet she manages, thus ensuring the continuation of her species.

Large brains and the ability to use tools don't necessarily amount to increased chances of survival – mosquitoes can transmit life-threatening diseases to humans, which has made for an uneasy relationship. But every species has its place in the web of life; though mosquitoes may eat us, or at least our blood, many other creatures eat them including bats, frogs, swallows and trout, who feed off the larvae in fresh water. Without mosquitoes, many other species would eventually die out.

And not all mosquitoes feed off blood: adults of the subfamily Toxorhynchites are purely vegetarian, while their larvae will predate other mosquito larvae.

A melting Arctic will be useful for the mosquitoes there as more mammals head northwards. Though of course they may find themselves competing with other mosquito species exploring new places to colonise.

Plight of the Arctic Mosquito

Chorus:
It's a hard life, it's a hard life,
Searching for food in a barren landscape
It's a hard life, it's a hard life,
Hunting for blood to nourish my eggs

V1
Flying around on my slender wings
Desperately searching for prey
My only goal to lay my eggs
Before death takes me away

Hated and feared by humankind
Because of the diseases I bear
They try to destroy me, forgetting that
I am food for others to share

Chorus

V2
As the ice caps melt and the permafrost dissolves
There'll be more stagnant ponds where we can thrive
We exist to explore every possible niche
Like all creatures, we aim to survive

We can bring down an army, destroy a city
Though we are fragile and small
As the nectar of warm mammal blood flows through us
We'll watch your civilisation fall....

Chorus

Plight of the Arctic Mosquito

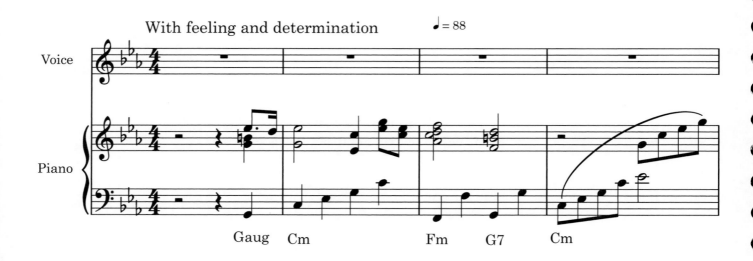

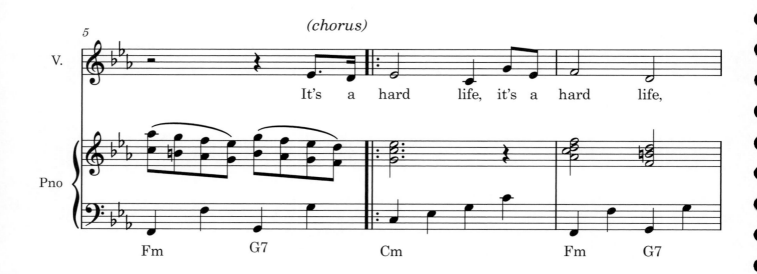

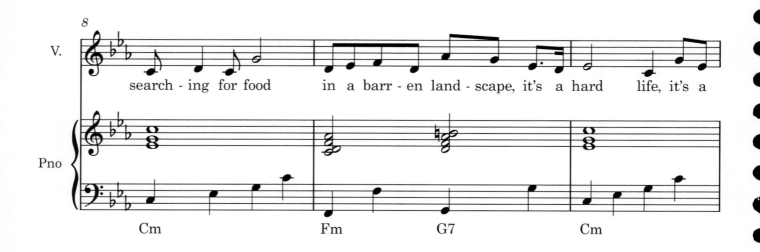

Plight of the Arctic Mosquito

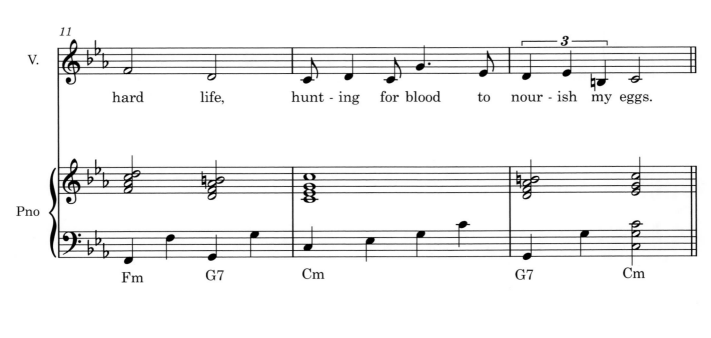

Plight of the Arctic Mosquito

Plight of the Arctic Mosquito

Plight of the Arctic Mosquito

thrive   We ex - ist to ex - plore ever - y poss - i - ble niche, like all

Fm6/D

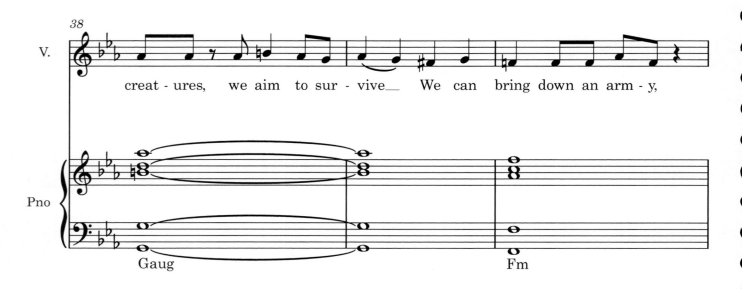

creat - ures,   we aim to sur - vive__   We can   bring down an arm - y,

Gaug   Fm

De - stroy a ci - ty,   Though we are fra - gile and small   As the

Plight of the Arctic Mosquito

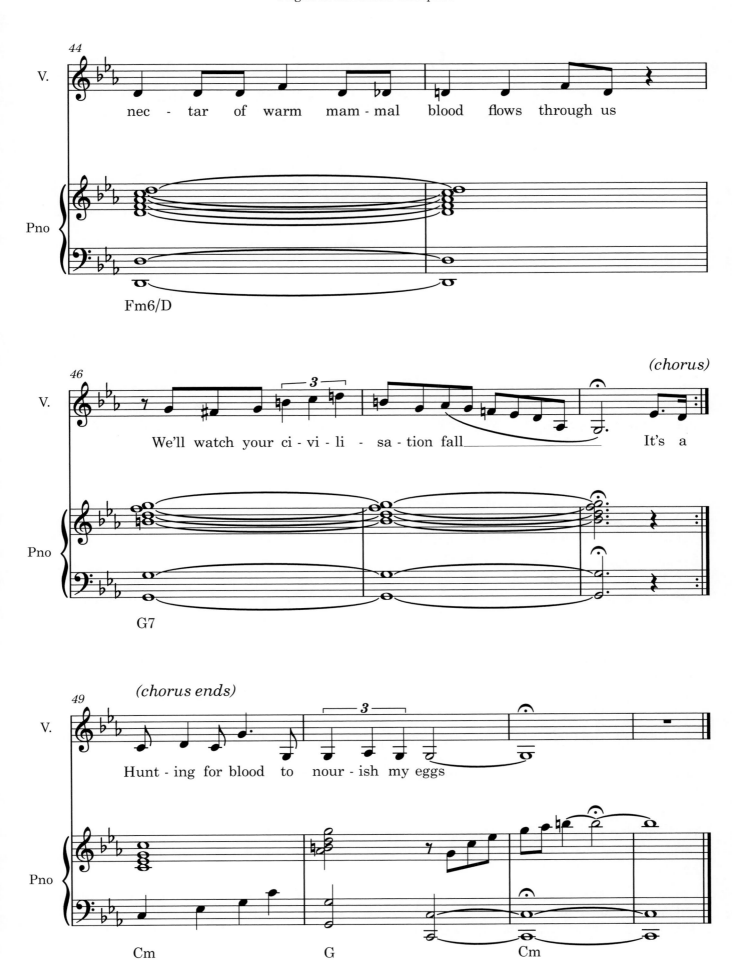

Chocolate

(the midge that pollinates it)

The cocoa midge belongs to the order Diptera, (meaning two-winged in Latin) – ie flies (see song of the same name). Its family is Ceratopogonidae – the 'biting midges' that include the notorious Scottish midges and many more that have successfully disrupted human activities all over the world. The cocoa midge is tiny enough to get inside the small cocoa flower, but it's challenging, as the flowers grow upside down directly out of the tree trunk, the flowers are awkward to get inside and only last for a day or two and the midge's capacities for flying and carrying pollen are limited.

The expression 'no see um' probably originated in North America in the 19th century, though exactly who first abbreviated it is unclear.

Chocolate is loved all over the world and has become big business, but cutting down rain forest and replacing it with plantations deprives the midges of their natural habitat – and if they disappear, what then? Well, enter Big Chocolate – the U.S. corporations Mars and Hershey. They have helped to fund the sequencing of the cocoa genome so that new strains of genetically modified chocolate can be developed to save the world. No need to save the rainforests! Just plant some new trees around plantations. Proponents of this plan claim that it will save struggling West African cocoa growers as rising temperatures adversely impact the cocoa plants, and there isn't time for normal cross-breeding as the plants take five years to grow to maturity (and anyway those midges are inefficient..) But actually it will make vast profits for the companies. And it certainly won't help the midges, who won't have the habitats they need to survive.

Big profits or tiny midges? Of course we love it when an animal benefits us (eg. ensuring a supply of chocolate) but if it conflicts with human plans, doesn't make enough money, or is capable of hurting us (midge bites can trigger allergic reactions, and midges themselves may transmit disease) species are deliberately destroyed or left to go extinct.

No UK midge will carry a really nasty disease, though they sometimes do in other parts of the world. If you're worried, or can't stand the itching, wear midge-proof head covering. At least you can breathe through it!

And remember, no mammal blood = no pollination = no chocolate (and lots of other plant foods)..it's our choice! Or do we just want to leave it to the corporations?

Chocolate
(the midge that pollinates it)

Chorus:
Oh chocolate, chocolate
The midge that pollinates it doesn't always make it
Chocolate, chocolate
We can't be sure there'll always be more

V1
Chocolate comes from the cocoa bean
Its flower is pollinated by a midge that's hardly seen
It's very very small and it can't fly far
A lot of effort goes into a chocolate bar!

Chorus

V2
The weather's changing and having effects
On all forms of life including insects
If you're small it's hard to fly
When storms are raging through the sky

Chorus

V3
Cocoa midges like damp and shade
They're not big fans of free trade
Plantations are too hot and dry
Wild forests are where they love to fly

Chorus

V4
However small a midge may be
It needs to eat like you and me
So don't begrudge the no see ums
Your blood – we need their pollination!

Chorus

Chocolate (the midge that pollinates it)

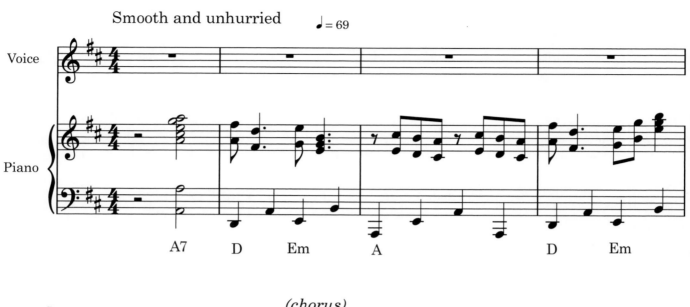

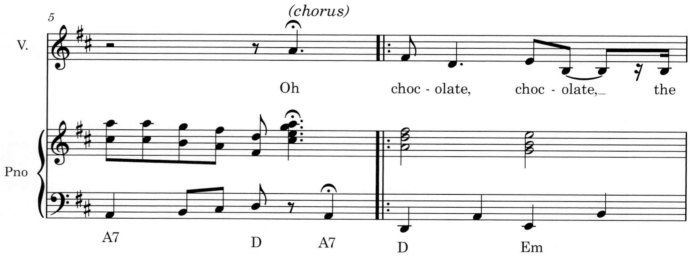

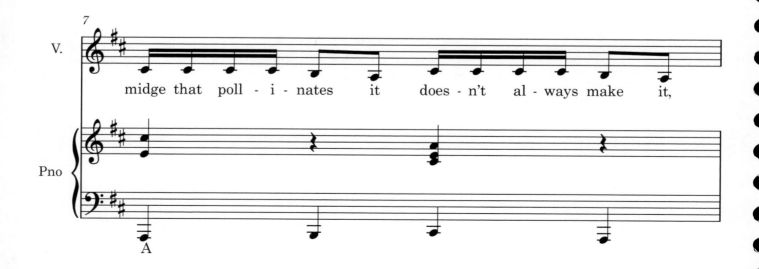

67

Chocolate (the midge that pollinates it)

(verse 1)

Chocolate (the midge that pollinates it)

Chocolate (the midge that pollinates it)

Chocolate (the midge that pollinates it)

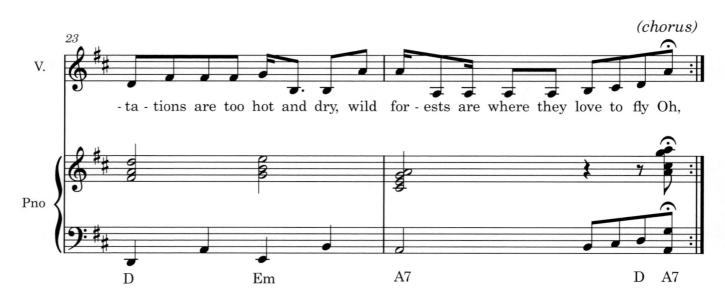

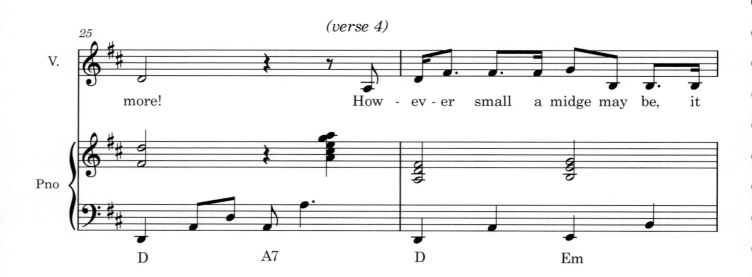

Chocolate (the midge that pollinates it)

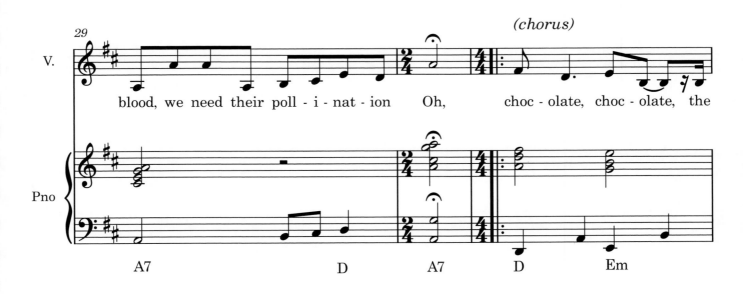

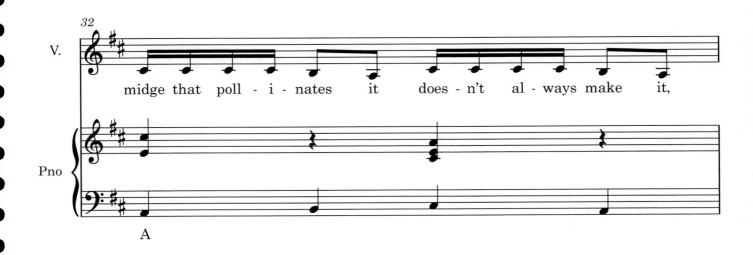

Chocolate (the midge that pollinates it)

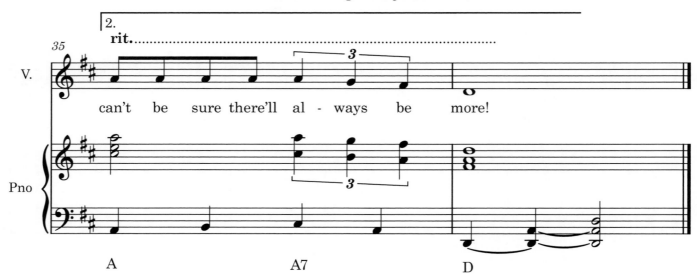

Grasshopper

Grasshoppers enliven summer days with their percussive music – which they make by rubbing their legs against their wings. Their sounds get quicker and louder as the temperature rises – you can notice that even if a cloud goes just briefly across the sun the grasshoppers will get quieter and slow down slightly.

They pick up vibrations via a membrane or 'ear drum' in their stomachs, which are transmitted to inner chambers in their bodies and translate into the sounds they hear – which must be so different to what we hear!

They are athletic - relative to its size, the average grasshopper can jump the equivalent length of a football pitch. Unlike crickets, they are vegetarian, although they may occasionally scavenge dead insects to supplement their diet. They eat a lot – up to 16 times their body weight.

There are over 10,000 species of grasshopper world-wide. They've been around for about 65 millions years before us, and their evolution coincides with the appearance of grasslands on earth. Yet they are present on all continents except Antarctica and some species are found in deserts.

Unfortunately, they can come into conflict with humans, as certain kinds of grasshopper can turn into locusts, which happens when too many are living too close together. Then they change colour, grow proper wings and take to the sky in those scary, all-devouring swarms described in the bible. Though mostly that happens outside Europe, 2020 saw a plague of locusts decimate crops in Sardinia. Another example of a creature becoming a 'pest' when humans are trying to farm. Some people eat them though – they're high in protein. Eat or be eaten!

Grasshopper

Introduction
Che che che che che che che che che che che che che che x2

Verse
Grasshopper, see me jump, grasshopper – see me play
Can you find me in the long grass, hidden on a sunny day?
Pretending I'm a twig or a leaf
On a warm summer day
Pretending I'm a twig or a leaf
On a warm summer day
Che che che che che che che che che che che che che che x2

Repeat whole verse

Can you find me? Che che che
Can you find me? Che che che
Can you find me on a warm summer day?
Can you find me? Che che che
Can you find me? Che che che
Can you find me? Che che che che che che che che che
(Half whisper) Can you find me?

Grasshopper

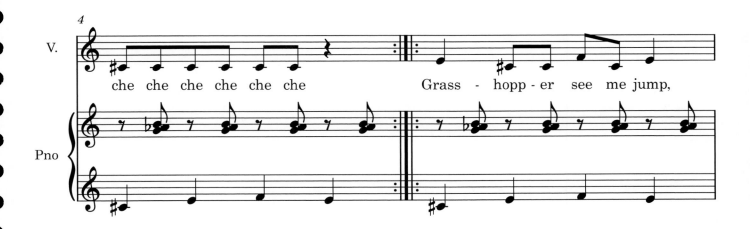

Grasshopper

Grasshopper

Grasshopper

(quieter second time)

Grasshopper

Praise the Beetles

The beetle order, Coleoptera, is currently known as the largest insect order. More species of beetle have been identified than any other order of insects. Their forewings are hardened, which means that although they are not such skilled fliers as eg.butterflies or true flies, they can also burrow underground or make their way through prickly vegetation that would damage the delicate wings of other winged insects. But most beetles can fly when needed.

Talking definitively of size is tricky, especially as sometimes an animal gets noticed that previously had been unheard of. The Featherwing beetle and the Fairy Fly (a tiny parasitic wasp) both jostle for position as the world's smallest insect but it seems the smallest beetle is smaller than the smallest wasp (about 0.25 cm).

The largest insect depends on how you measure, but the body length of the Atlas beetle is probably longest of all the beetles if you discount the horns. But of course, when they first evolved, all insects were massive in size compared to now because the earth's atmosphere was so full of oxygen. They only started to diminish as birds evolved.

J.B.S – John Burden Sanderson Haldane was a much respected British born scientist and mathematician who eventually settled in India. His fascination with the origins of life led him to the emerging science of genetics and he invented the term 'genetic soup'.

No-one is quite sure if he really said that God must have an inordinate fondness for beetles, but someone did – and there are 350,000 beetle species living on the earth compared to 10,000 mammal ones.

It's unlikely that Haldane would have called God 'she' either (he was born in 1892) – but you never know – he was a socialist.

Praise the Beetles

Oh...

Chorus:
Beetles, beetles, all over the world there are beetles
As Professor Haldane might have said
If there's a God – she's inordinately fond of beetles!

V1
Dung beetles, stag beetles, burial beetles, leaf beetles, ladybirds
Click beetles, nut weevils, tiger beetles, water beetles, bombardiers
Praise to evolution and the miracle of

Chorus

V2
Adapted to different habitats, they can breathe on earth or in water
Boring through wood, hiding in rocks, diving in the river
Only at the North and South poles will you find no

Chorus

V3
The smallest insect known so far is the Featherwing beetle
And among the largest is the Atlas beetle
Nearly half of all the insect world is made up of

Chorus

V4
Beetles in many clever ways confuse and avoid predators
Merging into leaves and bark with stripes and spots and colours
Or spraying acid from their backsides like the bombardier

Chorus

V6
The scarabs of ancient Egypt were worshipped and respected
Symbols of immortality, beloved of the sun god
For the grubs emerge from a pile of dung
As brilliant, shining

Chorus

last line (after one complete chorus):
And if there's a Heaven, it's surely full of wonderful, glorious beetles!

Praise the Beetles

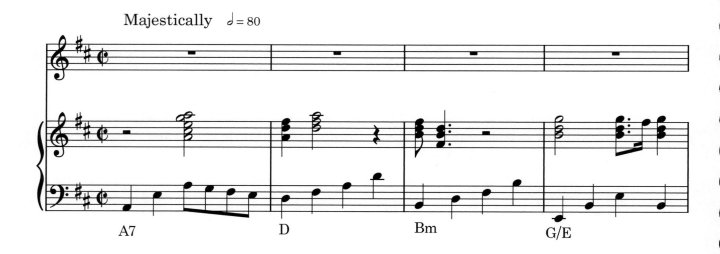

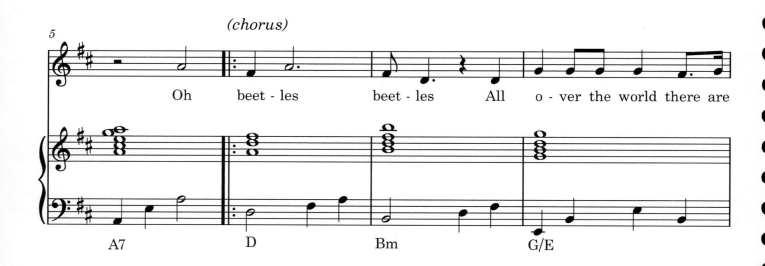

Oh beet - les beet - les All o - ver the world there are

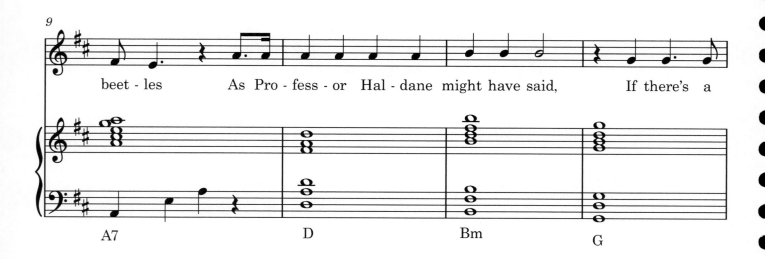

beet - les As Pro - fess - or Hal - dane might have said, If there's a

Praise the Beetles

Praise the Beetles

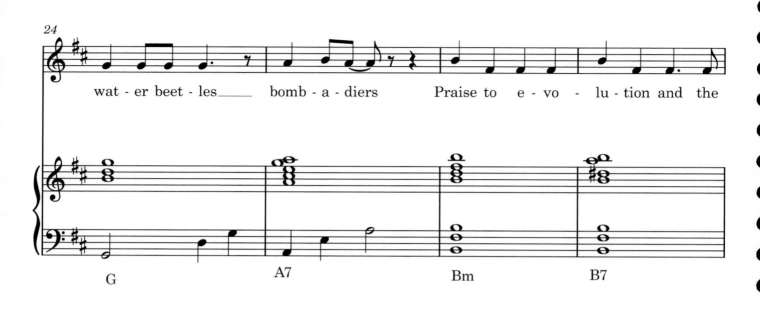

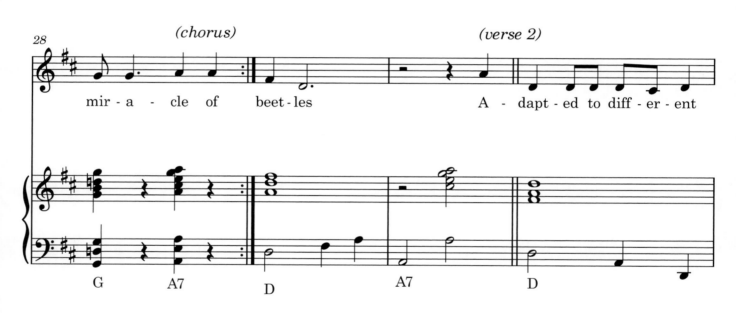

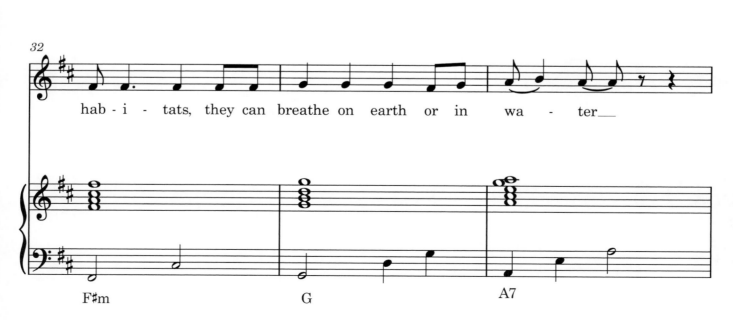

Praise the Beetles

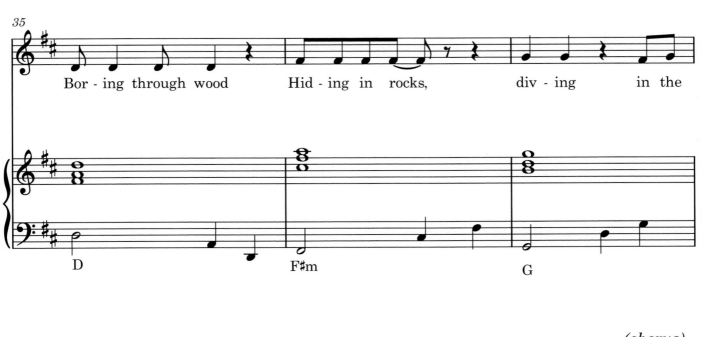

Bor - ing through wood Hid - ing in rocks, div - ing in the

D   F♯m   G

(chorus)

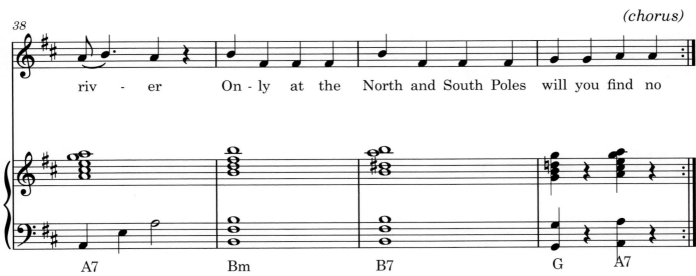

riv - er On - ly at the North and South Poles will you find no

A7   Bm   B7   G   A7

(verse 3)

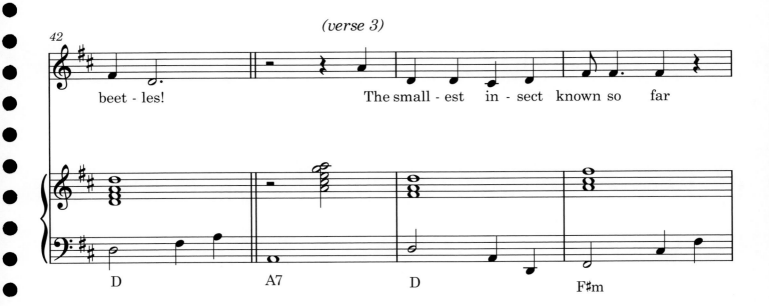

beet - les! The small - est in - sect known so far

D   A7   D   F♯m

Praise the Beetles

Praise the Beetles

Praise the Beetles

Praise the Beetles

Queen Bumble

There are at least 255 known species of bumble bee in the genus Bombus.

I was struck by the pressure an emerging new Queen Bumble is under – to start a whole new colony and make sure it survives the year. And she hasn't eaten for months! In a cold or wet spring it can be hard for bumble bees to find enough food to get going but they have evolved to survive lower temperatures and less light than other kinds of bee, including honey bees. So they're highly important pollinators as they can start earlier and keep going for longer. Their furry coats help to insulate them from the cold.

When she first comes out of her winter hibernation, the Queen needs to eat and warm up a bit to give her the strength to find a suitable nest – an old mousehole or thick tussock of grass will do nicely. And she can't start laying her eggs without some food inside her.

It's not true that bumble bee flight defies physics because the wings are so small relative to body size. For a start, bumble bees have two pairs of wings, and each front and rear wing is hooked together so they move in unison for better co-ordination. The bumble bee doesn't flap its wings up and down but forwards and backwards with a slight twist – almost like rowing through air. This lowers the air pressure above the wings and means the bee can stay aloft. Its wings beat about 200 times a second - that's a lot of work! So a bumble bee needs to keep eating to maintain its energy.

Bumble bees can only feed from flowers so they need habitats that are rich in flowering plants. Intensification of agriculture and use of insecticides caused bumble bee numbers to plummet during the 20th century. So however small a garden you may have, even a balcony, make sure to plant for the bees. They are wonderful animals and vital to human health because of the amount of pollination they do.

Queen Bumble

V1
Buzzing around on a warm spring day, I've been asleep for months and now
I'm hungry
Got to start a family, create a new colony, but I can't do it if I'm hungry
Burying myself in the first flowers of spring
Feeling the warmth of the sun on my wings
I fly, I fly

V2
I drink sweet nectar, then take some back with pollen I need for my nest
Mix pollen and wax, and build a mound where I can lay my eggs
Sipping on my nectar pot as I wait
Shivering my wings as the eggs incubate
I wait, I wait

V3
When the grubs emerge I forage for food to nourish them as they grow
Then they spin cocoons where they change shape, while I come and go
My first-born daughters are workers, and so
My remaining task is to make the colony grow
To grow, grow

V4
I lay eggs while my daughters work, cleaning and finding food
I stay put, filling the nest with brood after brood
Workers, young queens, and lazy drones
All have their place in the home
The home, home

V5
As summer ends, the new queens mate, feed well, and stay alive
But my time's done, I'm old and bald - I'll die with the rest of my hive
The young queens will sleep the winter through
Then one sunny day they'll emerge and look for food
And fly, fly, fly.....

Queen Bumble

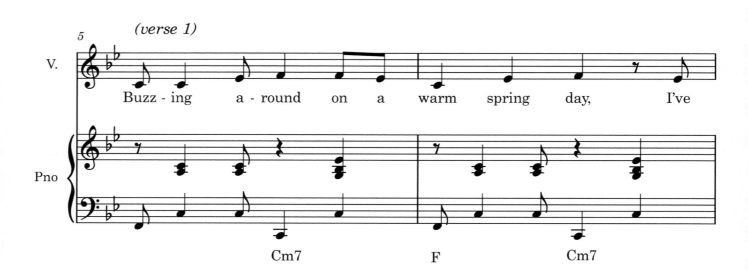

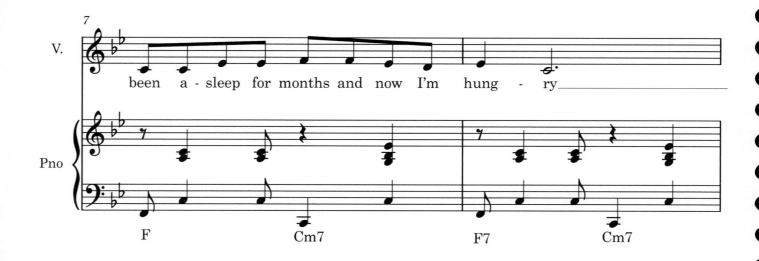

Queen Bumble

Queen Bumble

Queen Bumble

Queen Bumble

Queen Bumble

Queen Bumble

Queen Bumble

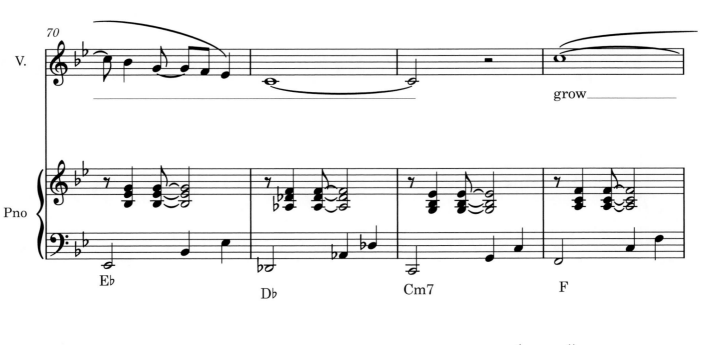

grow

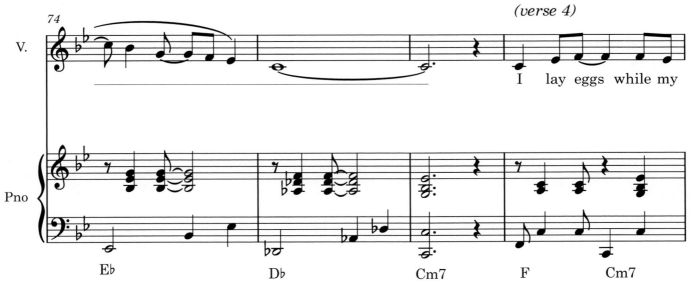

(verse 4)

I lay eggs while my

daught-ers work   clean-ing and find-ing   food

Queen Bumble

Queen Bumble

Queen Bumble

Queen Bumble

Queen Bumble

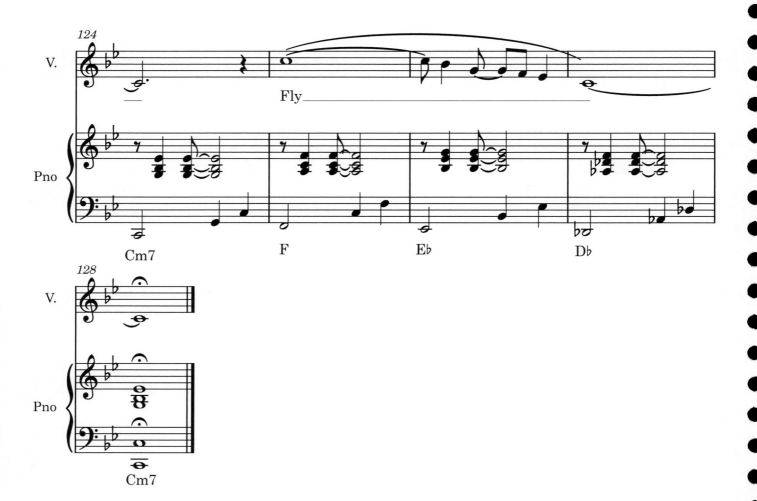

Good Connections

Taxonomy is a tricky subject - and classifications keep changing - but here goes:

> Kingdom – Animalia
> Phylum - Arthropoda
> Class – Insecta
> Order – eg Lepidoptera (butterflies and moths)
> Possibly a Superfamily! Eg Papilionoidea (true butterflies)
> Family – eg Nymphalidae
> Genus – eg Inachis Io
> Species eg European Peacock butterfly or Aglais Io

Regardless of one's skill in memorising any of this, just looking through the classifications does give a glimpse of the enormous complexity, diversity and intricacy of life's relationships on earth. And yes! - we are family - we all came from those original single celled organisms that started up on earth a few billion years ago...and before that from the elements in space..and before that...?

Good Connections

V1
Let's sing about our cousins Insecta
Part of the phylum Arthropoda
Species, family and order
All contained in Animalia

Chorus
Family, family, with good connections
Doing its thing with a little bit of help from
Natural Selection

V2
Odonata, Ephemeroptera
Diptera, Paleoptera
Collembola, Coleoptera
Phthiraptera, Lepidoptera

V3
Dragonflies, mayflies and general flies
Ancient insects of all kinds
Springtails, beetles, and all lice
Moths and butterflies

Chorus

V4
Cockroaches – Blattodea
Earwigs – Dermoptera
Then sawflies, ants, wasps and bees
Are all in Hymenoptera

V5
Let's hear it for Isoptera – termites!
And Orthoptera – grasshoppers!
Thrips are Thysanoptera, booklice – Psocoptera!

V6
Odonata, Ephemeroptera, Diptera, Paleoptera
Collembola, Coleoptera, Phthiraptera, Lepidoptera
Blattodea, Dermoptera, Hymenoptera
Isoptera, Orthoptera, Thysanoptera, Psocoptera!

Chorus x1 then

Family, family, with good connections
Just remember that – we are all relations!

Good Connections

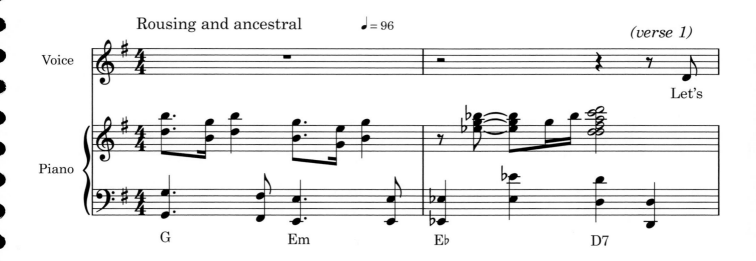

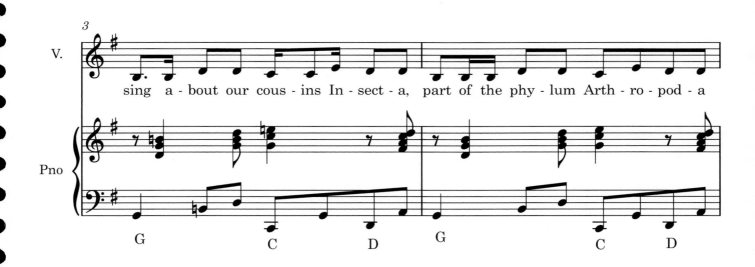

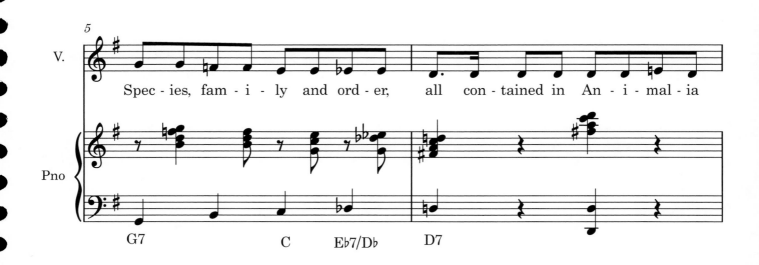

Good Connections

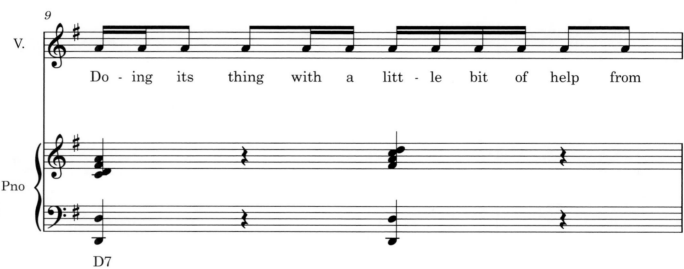

Good Connections

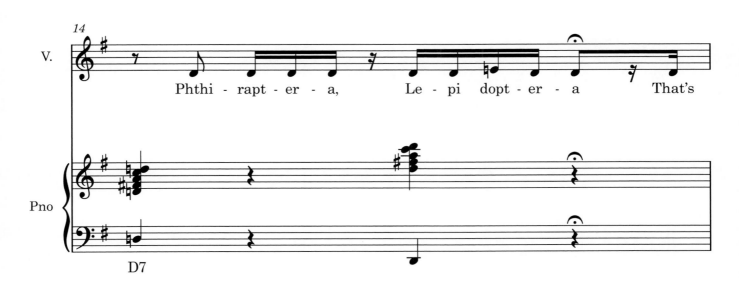

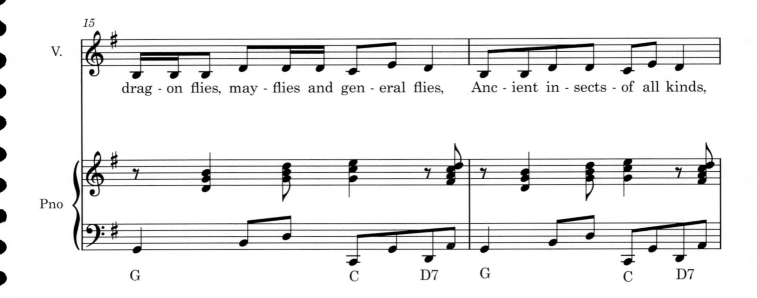

Good Connections

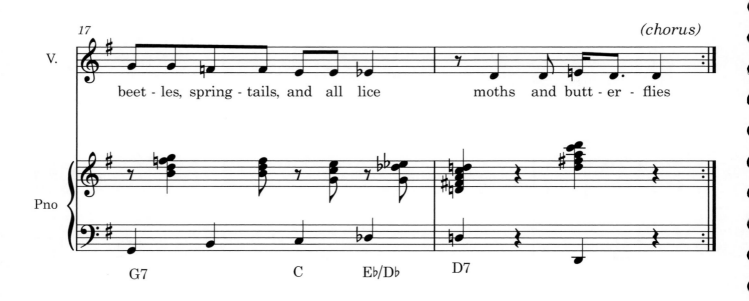

(chorus)

17

V.

beet - les, spring - tails, and all lice moths and butt - er - flies

Pno

G7   C   Eb/Db   D7

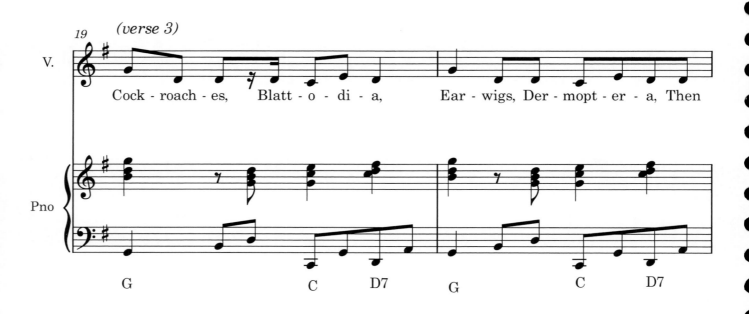

(verse 3)

19

V.

Cock - roach - es, Blatt - o - di - a, Ear - wigs, Der - mopt - er - a, Then

Pno

G   C   D7   G   C   D7

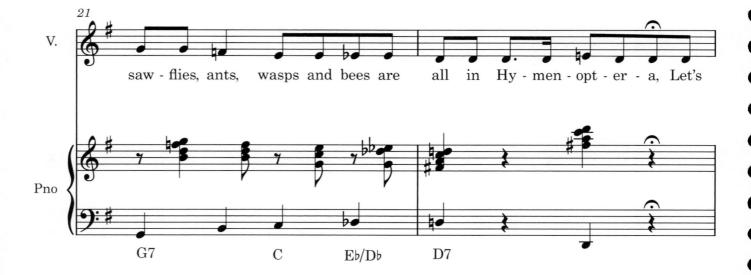

21

V.

saw - flies, ants, wasps and bees are all in Hy - men - opt - er - a, Let's

Pno

G7   C   Eb/Db   D7

Good Connections

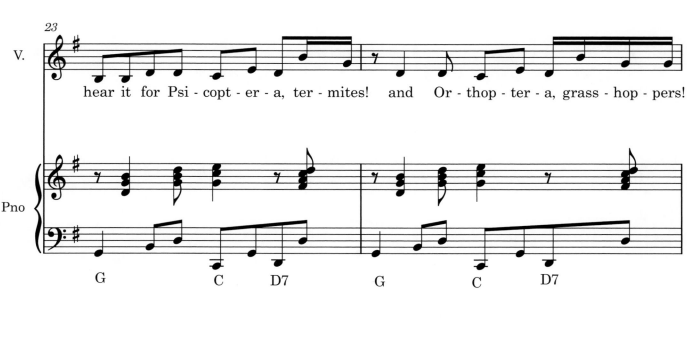

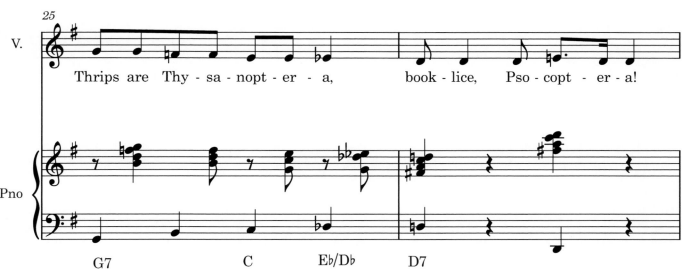

112

Good Connections

113

Good Connections

Good Connections

How Many Legs?

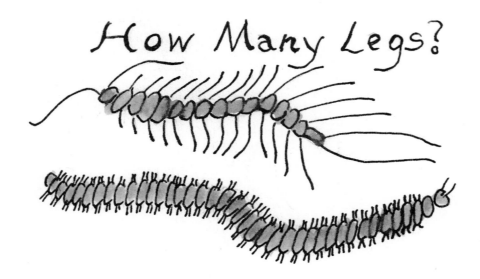

Some very patient person must have spent many hours counting the legs on centipedes and millipedes. But obviously there's more counting to be done as no-one is exactly sure how many they really have.

It turns out that millipedes usually have more, as they have two pairs of legs per body segment, mostly between 200 -300 but occasionally up to about 750 in all. But recently a millipede boasting no less than 1,306 legs has been found living a couple of hundred feet underground in Western Australia. Centipedes can have anything from 35 to just under 200.

Both millipedes and centipedes are born with just a few pairs of legs, but each time they moult – and they moult a lot – they add a segment and more legs. Centipedes move fast, forwards and backwards, and each pair of legs is a bit longer then the pair in front so they don't trip up. Millipedes just move along slowly with a wave-like motion.

Their characters are so different – centipedes are fast and nervous – if you find them in the soil they wriggle away fast, and they are highly predatory – they'll even eat other centipedes. They have front claws and can be venomous. Slow-moving millipedes however are mostly peaceful and vegetarian, though some are capable of producing a foul-smelling, stinging ooze to deter predators. They can be prey for many creatures including toads, spiders and birds. For such small animals, they can live a long time if they don't get eaten – up to about a decade for some millipedes, and one to about five years for centipedes. When wooing a female, a male millipede may croon (or rather play) a love song, or give his beloved a back massage, as otherwise she may get nervous and curl into a ball. Centipedes do not massage each other but may do an elegant courtship dance involving legs and antennae.

Both millipedes and centipedes evolved to live on the land over 400 million years ago, and would have been scarily much bigger then.

There are thousands of species of centipedes world-wide, and tens of thousands of millipedes.

Time to start counting those legs!

How Many Legs?

Chorus:
How many legs, how many legs
How many legs, how many legs?

V1
If I move at lightning speed, that means I'm a centipede
I will chase and bite my dinner, and my body's slightly thinner

Chorus

V2
If I move quite slowly, and I'm rather muscle-y
Tube-shaped and chunky, then milli, millipede that's me

Chorus

V3
Millipede or centipede, it all depends on how you feed
How you move and how you feel, and do you roll into a ball?
Are your legs short or long, are you rather highly-strung?
Do you chase and bite your dinner – or are you vegetarian?

Chorus, keep repeating and fade out

How Many Legs?

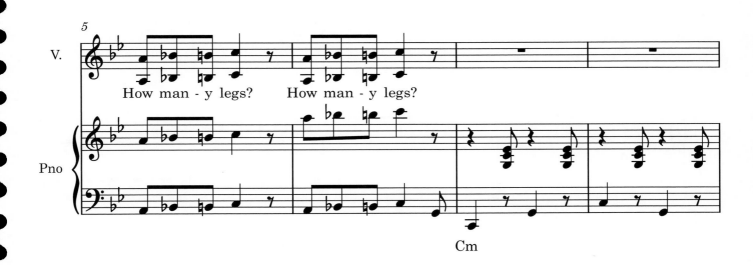

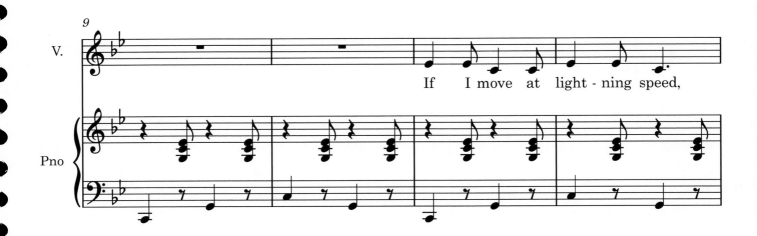

How Many Legs?

How Many Legs?

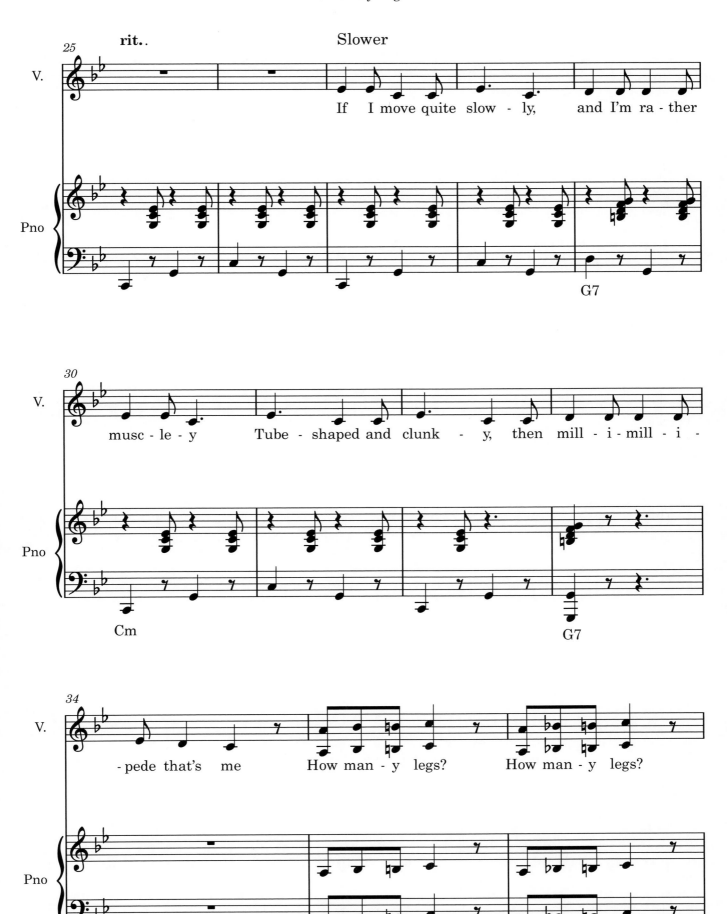

120

How Many Legs?

How Many Legs?

How Many Legs?

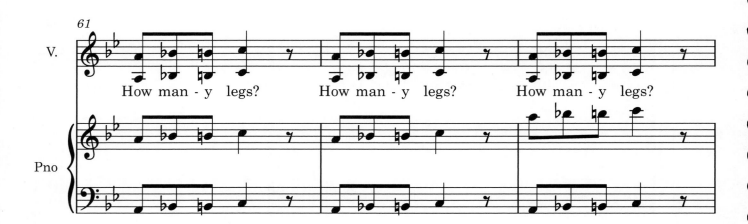

Woodlouse

Woodlice are crustaceans – like shrimps and crabs - and came onto land from the sea, probably during the Carboniferous era. They are found all over the world, except for the Arctic and the most arid regions of desert. They need moisture to breathe, which they do through gill-like appendages on their legs. One species has however evolved to survive desert conditions.

They keep growing and have to shed their skin/moult regularly, but, to lessen their vulnerability, they moult in two stages, front and then back half (they have 11 segments so that's quite a lot of moulting).

They are innocuous animals but sometimes disturb humans as they can get into houses and cluster in nooks and crannies – they like to keep damp, as they lose moisture through their outer cuticles and dry out very rapidly, but cannot survive flooding.

Why they have so many popular names is curious, or why these names are so often linked to pigs eg grammasows, slunker pigs. Maybe being a ubiquitous harmless animal makes people want to name you.

Woodlouse

V1
I'm an isopod, with seven pairs of legs
An ancient relative of lobsters, shrimp and crab
When you find me hiding under a stone
Don't be alarmed – I'm no harm to anyone

V2
I have many cousins, in the sea and on the land
And why some people hate my kind, I don't quite understand
I feed off rotten wood and help things decompose
I won't attack your furniture or gobble up your toes

V3
There's threats all around, so I have to stay alert
Don't want to get dried out, or be squished into the dirt.
I'd rather not be breakfast for a hedgehog or a toad
Or indeed – supper for a centipede!

V4
I'm shy and retiring, but I have a suit of armour
And I keep on changing it as I grow bigger
I can roll into a ball if I get a fright
And prefer to hide away from the bright sunlight

V5
I like to stay in the damp and dark, so that I can breathe
I potter about at night, and I'm good for your compost heap.
I've been called all sorts of names like chisel-hog, or monkey-pea
But I just want to live in peace, so please be kind to me

Woodlouse

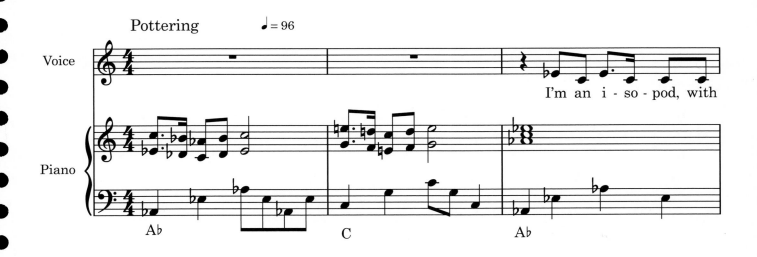

Pottering   ♩ = 96

Voice / Piano

I'm an i - so - pod, with

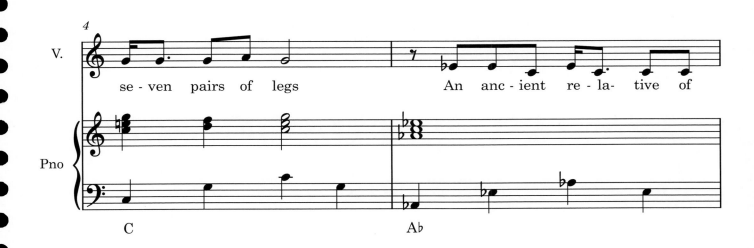

se - ven pairs of legs   An anc - ient re - la - tive of

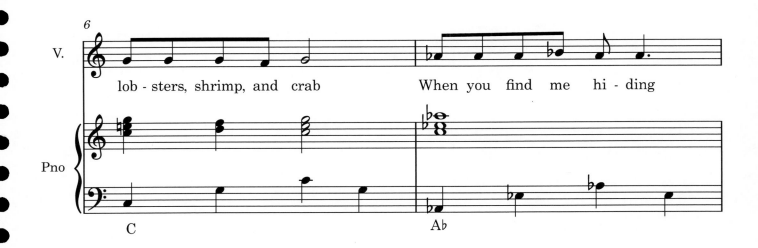

lob - sters, shrimp, and crab   When you find me hi - ding

126

Woodlouse

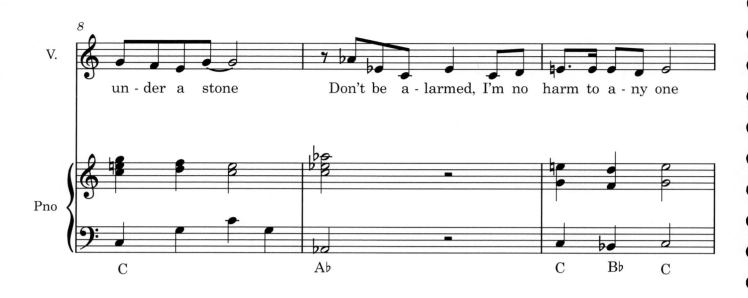

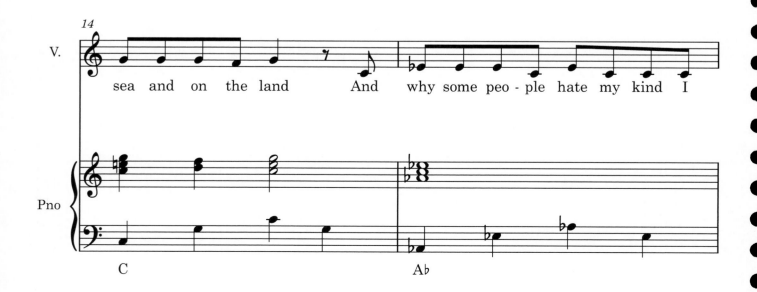

Woodlouse

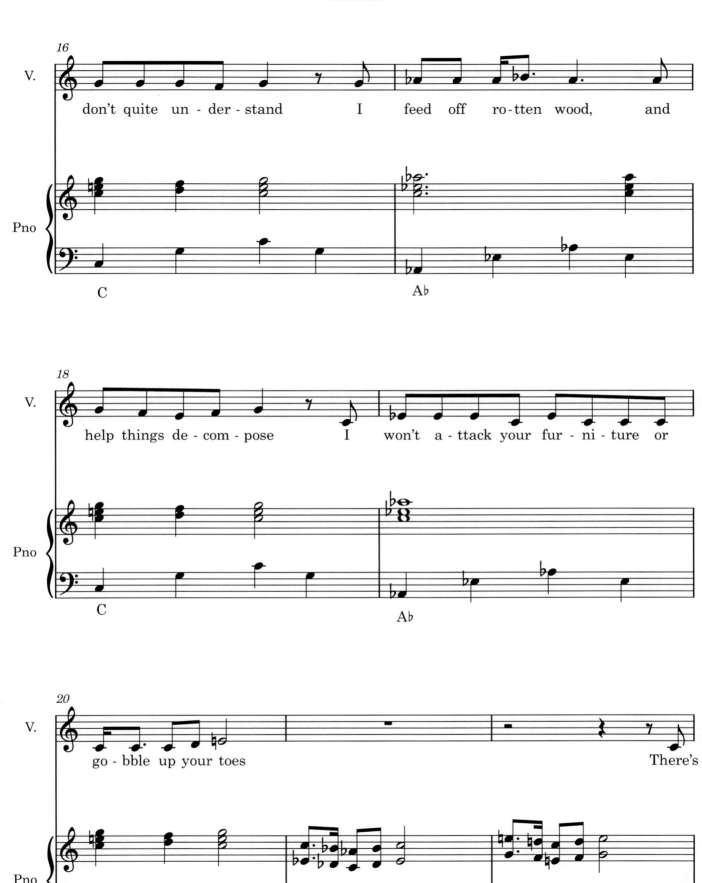

Woodlouse

Woodlouse

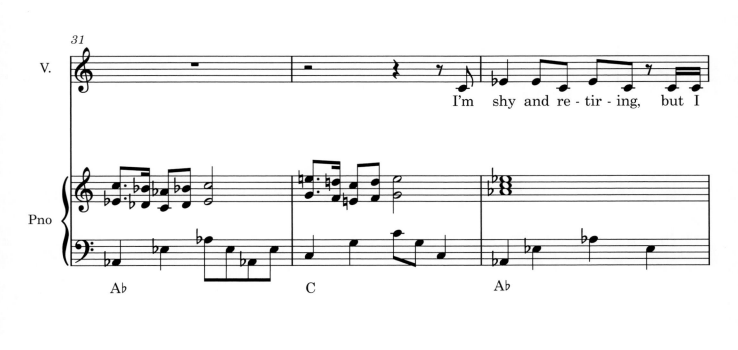

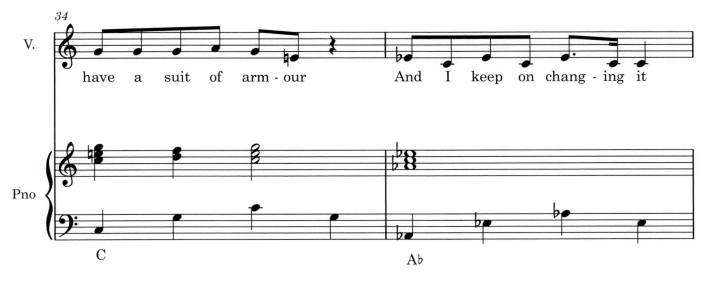

Woodlouse

Woodlouse

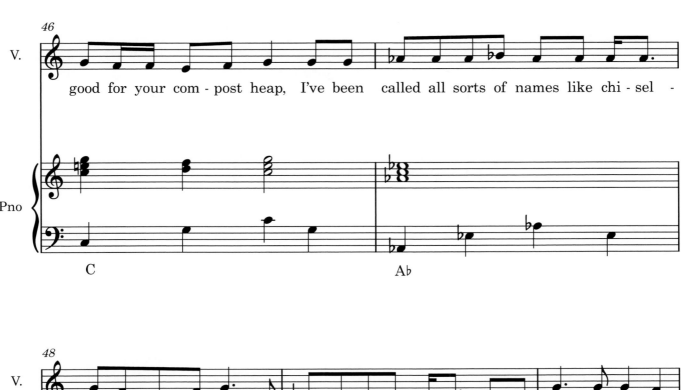

good for your com - post heap, I've been called all sorts of names like chi - sel -

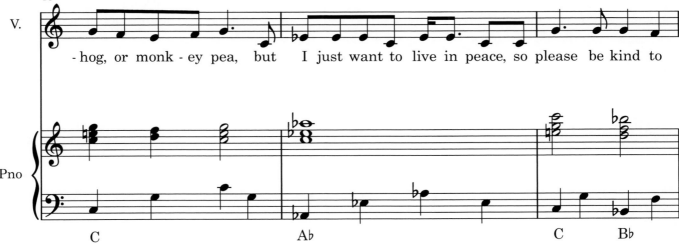

- hog, or monk - ey pea, but I just want to live in peace, so please be kind to

me!

Spiders, Spiders

Spiders are arthropods but they are not insects. There are two main groupings, the 'micro' which are mainly money spiders (family Linyphiidae) and all the rest - the 'macro'. There are about 670 species in the UK, which is low compared to the rest of Europe.

Spiders are another creature that many humans fear, but in the UK there are no deadly poisonous spiders, and few people hospitalised by a spider bite. Compare this with the number of people regularly admitted to hospital who have been badly injured by dog bites.

The Noble False Widow spider arrived in Britain in 1879 in a crate of bananas from the Canary Islands. A bite from one of these can land someone in hospital if they are unlucky. But despite media exaggeration they are not really venomous (though they do tend to eat their husbands after mating).

House spiders eat all sorts of flies and small insects that humans prefer not to have in the house. They are friends to gardeners too, as they will eat aphids and other potentially annoying flying insects.

Spiders can travel far - some spiders have been discovered floating high above the earth in the troposphere.

All spiders spin silk, but not all of them make webs, and different species produce different kinds of silk. Spider silk is extraordinarily strong and flexible – human scientists are creating new materials inspired by spider silk. It was the silk of Black Widow spiders (a venomous spider that inhabits temperate regions of the earth, but not generally N. Europe), that was collected in the USA to make gun cross hairs during WW2. It was not very pleasant for the spiders, who were forced to produce an unnatural quantity of silk in a short space of time, and as a result did not live as long as normal.

Spiders can alter the speed at which they spin to create different kinds of thread, and can 'tune' their webs so that they can recognise potential prey or visitors by the kind of vibration make. Spiders don't see very well but are highly sensitive to vibrations. Webs and silk may be used to catch prey, to make family dwellings, or to wrap up gifts (eg tasty flies) that a male spider might take when wooing a lover.

Spiders are wonderful and deserve respect.

Spiders, spiders

Chorus
Spiders, spiders, in all different sizes
We're not that poisonous, so don't be afraid of us
Few of us sting as badly as a bee
So don't do anything nasty to me!

V1
The silk that we spin is fine and strong
We use it to help us float along
Or to catch our dinner as it passes by
So we have the strength to climb to the sky
Chorus

V2
Are you put off by legs that are hairy?
Well, a spider can't shave to look less scary
If you find me in your bath – just be polite
Pick me up gently and set me right
Chorus

V3
I can fast for months, but when I eat
I can keep on going till I'm replete
My stomach swells, you think I'd pop
But I know exactly when to stop
Chorus

V4
Some of our behaviour is quite enthralling
Some of it humans may find appalling
Eating your neighbour is not what you do
But a spider may eat her husband too!
Chorus

Spiders, spiders

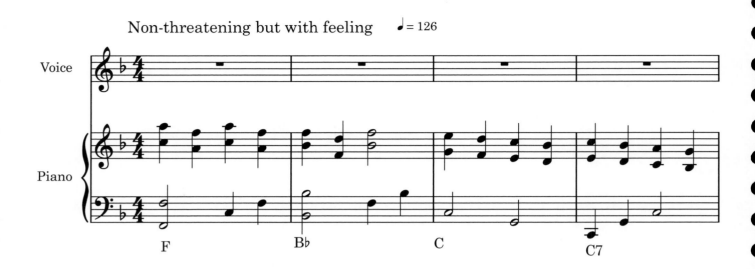

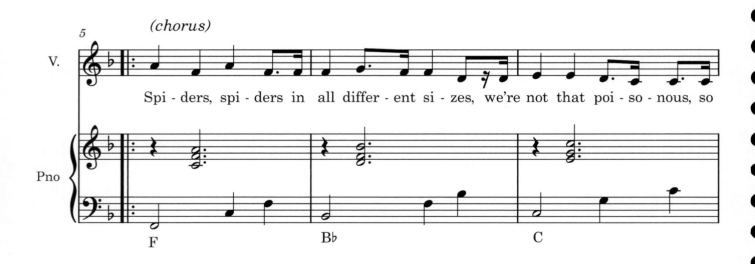

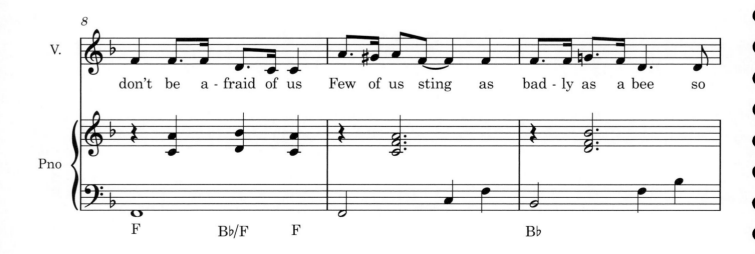

Spiders, spiders

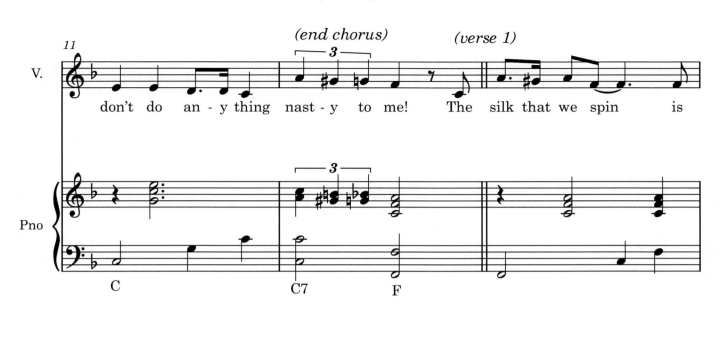

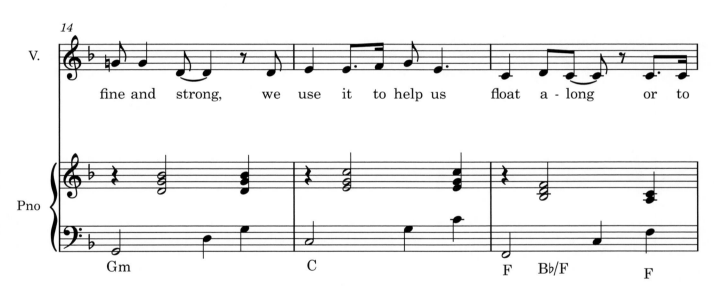

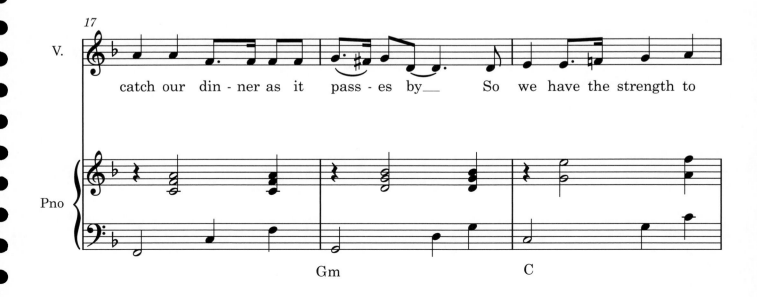

Spiders, spiders

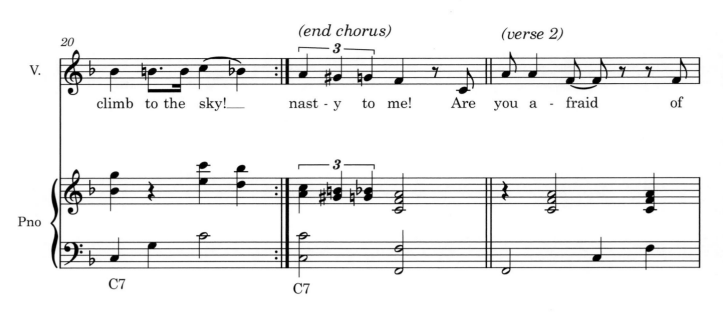

(end chorus) *(verse 2)*

climb to the sky!__ nast - y to me! Are you a - fraid of

C7   C7

legs that are hair - y? Well, a spi - der can't shave to look less scar - y, If you

Gm   C   F   Bb/F   F

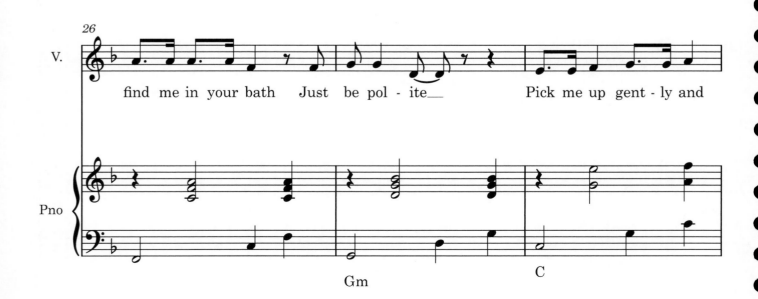

find me in your bath   Just be pol - ite__   Pick me up gent - ly and

Gm   C

Spiders, spiders

Spiders, spiders

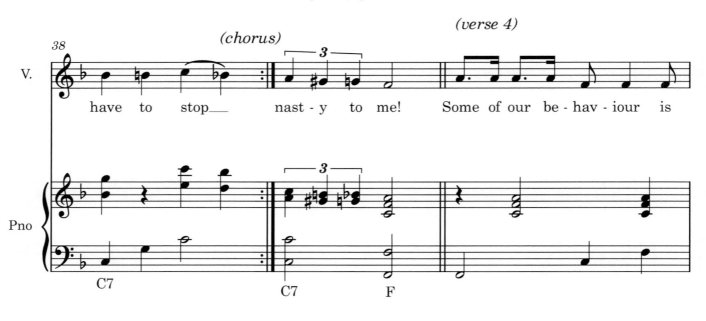

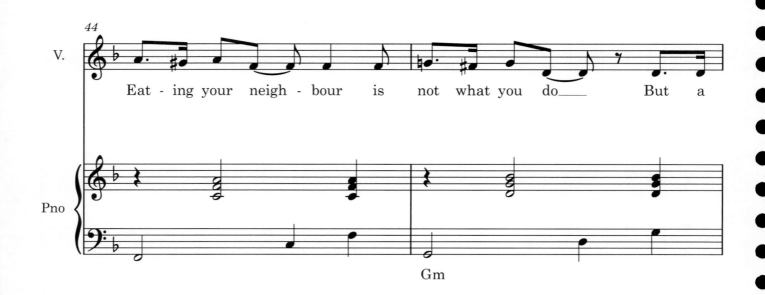

Spiders, spiders

According to Charles Darwin, 'there are few animals which have played so important a part in the history of the world than the earthworm'.

Darwin studied the lives of earthworms for over forty years, and his book The Formation of Vegetable Mould through the Action of Worms, with Observations on their Habits, initially outsold the Origin of Species when first published in 1881.

He carefully observed how earthworms shift soil and can eventually cause large stones and buildings to sink; he measured worm casts and put a 'worm stone' in his garden, watching as it was slowly buried over time. He estimated that earthworms shift fifteen tons of soil to the surface per acre of land. They also take leaves and other plant matter below the surface thus sequestering carbon. They are amazing creatures, friends to gardeners, and vital in maintaining and managing soil health.

By dint of playing loud music and even shouting at the earthworms he collected to study indoors, Darwin realised that they have no sense of hearing. However they are very sensitive to vibrations, reacting to the sounds of a piano when they were put on top of it in pots.

'Worm charming' is the art of coaxing worms to the surface by stamping or otherwise causing the soil to vibrate. No-one is exactly sure why the worms react in this way but they might be trying to avoid being hunted and eaten by moles. Birds have learned to vibrate their feet on the ground and lure out unfortunate earthworms into their waiting beaks when they want a snack.

Earthworms are amazing – they are the gardener's friend - and yet we still don't fully understand them or know how many different kinds there are.

Earthworms

V1
Earthworms, turning turning turning
Turning, composting and fertilising
All over the world

V2
Earthworms, nourishing and digesting
Every kind of soil and landscape
Protectors of the earth

V3
Earthworms, turning turning turning
Turning, moving air and water
Helping life along

V4
Earthworms, food for moles and baby foxes,
Loved by gardeners and growers
Keepers of the soil

(as round)
Earthworms, turning turning turning
ends All over the world

Earthworms

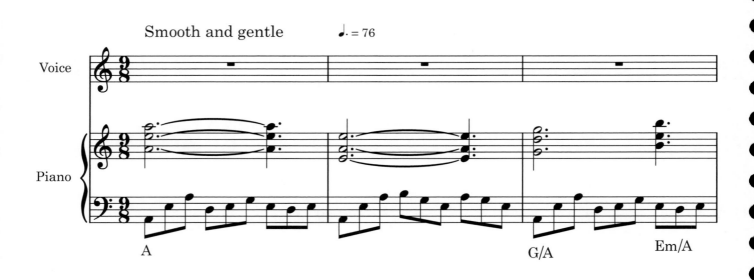

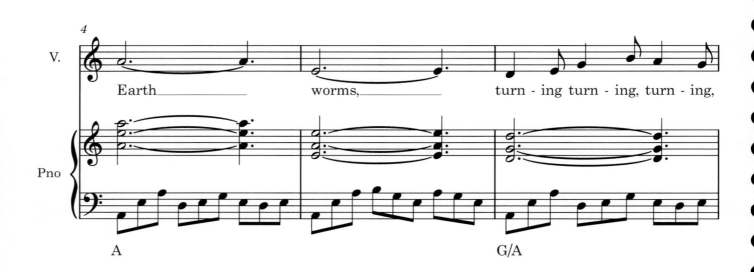

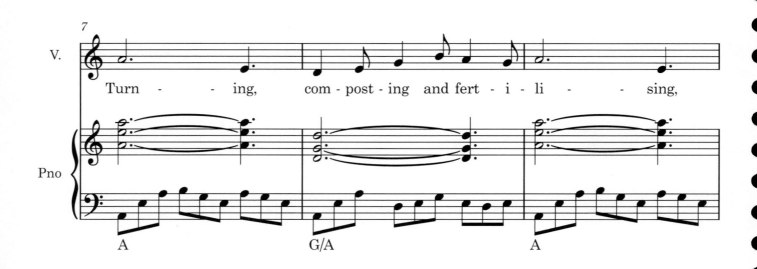

Earthworms

Earthworms

Earthworms

Earthworms

I'm a Snail

Snails and slugs belong to the Phylum Mollusca, which includes cuttlefish and octopus.

Originally all molluscs lived in the sea - and apart from the bivalves they all have a radula ('little scraper' in Latin) - a ribbon-like tongue with thousands of tiny sharp chitinous teeth on it. And yes, these teeth are renewable – snails don't need fillings or false teeth!

There are land snails, freshwater snails and snails that still live in the sea.

Most land snails are vegetarian, and as every gardener knows, the garden snail can make short work of fresh young plants and seedlings. But they also eat dead animals and dead plant material and so stop lots of decaying matter piling up. They will also eat fungi, and occasionally nibble bits of chalk for calcium to make their shells stronger. Sea snails will eat small marine animals including other snails, freshwater snails occasionally eat small algae but are mainly vegetarian.

They all produce different kinds of slime.

For land-living snails, slime on their single foot helps them glide along and also attach themselves to hard surfaces, so they can climb up the walls of your house for example. Slime also keeps their bodies lubricated so they don't dry out - but they try to avoid hot sun and are mostly nocturnal.

In drought conditions a snail can 'estivate' and go dormant, plugging its shell with dried slime to protect its soft body within.

A snail can and does retreat into its shell when threatened, but a vigorous bash from a hungry blackbird or thrush and it's game over. But they have their slime to fall back on. Different chemicals in snail slime can make them taste so disgusting a predator will back off.

More about slime later in relation to slugs, but scientists are already interested in the antibiotic properties of garden snails' slime, and using it to replace stitches after surgery.

The largest known snail is probably the African Land snail, which grow up to 20 cm. The largest sea snail is even bigger – the Australian trumpet can reach up to 91 cm or 36 inches.

I'm a Snail

Chorus:
I'm a snail, I'm a snail
My teeth will never fail
Unlike you, I grow new ones as I chew
I'm a snail, I'm a snail
With my tentacles and tail
If you threaten me, I'll spew lots of goo!

V1
There are many who would eat
Me for a treat
I'll be cruelly attacked by a song thrush for a snack
But I have my strategy - to get amazingly gooey
And stick their beaks up with a gob of glue!

Chorus

V2
My touchy-feely tentacles sniff out delicious meals
When I come out at night I can tell it's dark, not light
I breathe gently through my skin, or, if I need to get more air in
A gulp into my breathing pore will do

Chorus

V3
If there is great heat, or a deadly chill
I can retreat into my shell
My love affairs are intricate
Because I am hermaphrodite
I lay eggs and I fertilise them too

Chorus

V4
Beetles are bad news for me, glow worms are my enemy
They eat me up or leave me paralysed
Oh let me gracefully glide
And find places to hide as I
Share all the vegetables you prize!

Chorus, plus optional chorus in Italian

Lumaca, lumaca
I denti non mi casca
Ricrescano mentre mastico
Lumaca, lumaca
Con tentaculi e coda
Se minaccii
Buto fuori tanta bava!

I'm a Snail

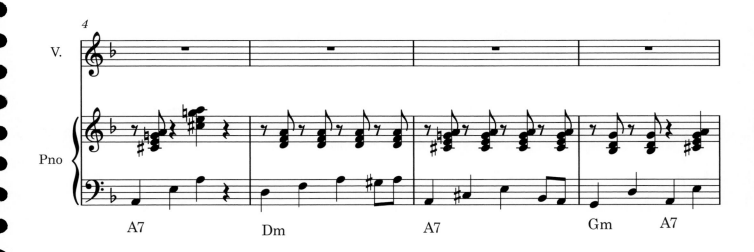

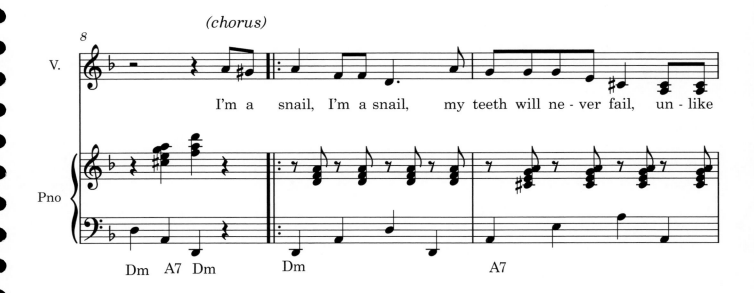

(chorus)

I'm a snail, I'm a snail, my teeth will ne - ver fail, un - like

I'm a Snail

(verse 1)

I'm a Snail

I'm a Snail

I'm a Snail

(repeat chorus)

gulp in - to my breath - ing pore will do   I'm a   goo!

Gm   A7   Dm

(verse 3)

If there is great heat   or a dead - ly chill   I can re - treat in -

Dm   Gm

- to my   shell   My love a - ffairs are in - tri - cate, be -

A7   Dm

I'm a Snail

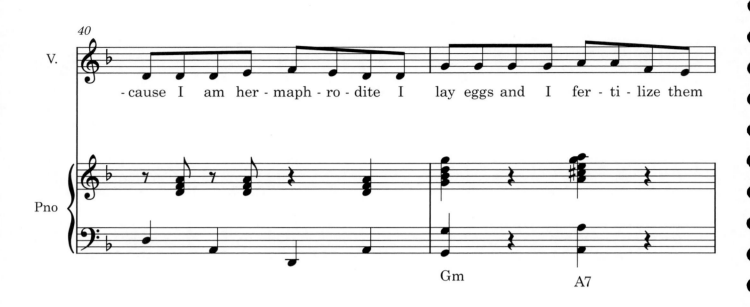

-cause I am her-maph-ro-dite I lay eggs and I fer-ti-lize them too.

Gm   A7

(repeat chorus)   *(verse 4)*

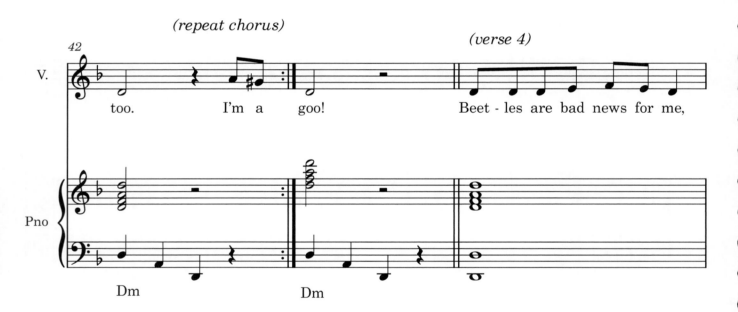

too.   I'm a   goo!   Beet-les are bad news for me,

Dm   Dm

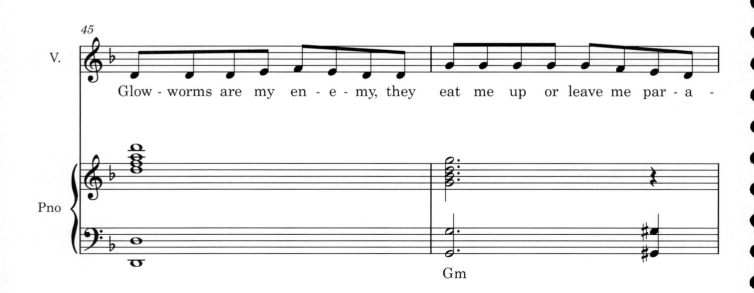

Glow-worms are my en-e-my, they eat me up or leave me par-a-

Gm

I'm a Snail

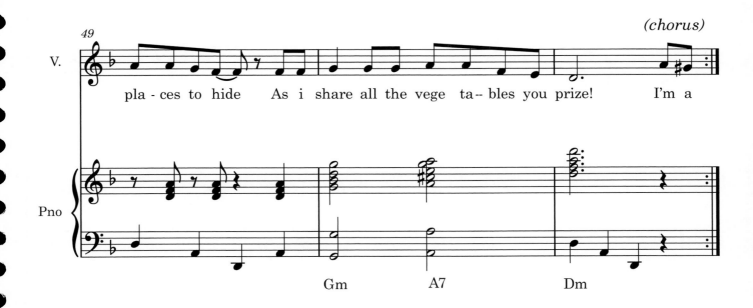

I'm a Snail

Soliloquy of the Slug

It's probably harder to be a slug than a snail – not even a thin shell to protect you. So slug slime tends to be even thicker and gooier than snail slime. As with snails, slugs' goo serves different purposes; it helps locomotion, it keeps the body moist when moving, or acts as glue when the slug is stationary, and it can also be a form of communication – a slug may follow another slug's slime trail in search of a mate. Then should two slugs fall in love, they produce a cord from which they hang suspended, sometimes for many hours. Slug goo can make it hard for a predator to get hold of it firmly enough to eat, and it may taste disgusting so they will drop it.

Slugs are often disliked, even feared, partly because they are so different to us and almost alien. But they are as vital to our ecosystem as all the other species. Other animals like to eat them if they can work out how to avoid the goo. Yes, like snails, slugs do have a taste for young tender plants, but they mainly chew up decomposing plant matter, thus storing carbon in the ground and keeping the soil nourished and aerated. They are happy in compost heaps. Some slugs, like the handsome Leopard slug, will eat other slugs so are definitely an asset to gardeners.

Notwithstanding, roughly 400 billion tons of slug pellets are used by UK farmers and growers each year and some of them are highly toxic. Metaldehyde, for example, kills domestic and wild animals, including hedgehogs and frogs – both of which eat slugs - and whose numbers are in sharp decline in the UK.

An attempt to ban slug pellets containing metaldehyde was overturned in 2019, but is supposed to become law again by 2022. Companies make good profits from selling poison.

Now that slug slime has been found to have wound-healing, cosmetic and skin-nourishing properties for humans, what next? Will it change attitudes to slugs, or make them even more vulnerable to slug-hunters who want to exploit them for financial gain?

Soliloquy of the Slug

V1
It's hard to be an animal hated by so many humans
With no hard shell to protect you, no poisonous sting to defend you
Just a soft sticky mass, eating all the tender plants it can find
And leaving lots of empty holes behind

Chorus:
It's a difficult thing to be a slug
When your home's on land that humans have dug
And they come after you with chemicals and salt or traps of beer
Enough to make your tentacles quiver with fear!

V2
We're food for many creatures, including slow worms and hedgehogs
With our slime we can ward off irritating dogs
Our whole body is sensitive to smell and taste
And we recycle all kinds of unpleasant, unwanted waste

Chorus

V3
We have about twenty seven thousand teeth that we constantly renew
The copper in our blood makes it greenish blue
We conduct electricity, and the earth's magnetic fields guide our way
As we lay down our gleaming trails of slime over night and day

Chorus

V4
A scientist discovered our slime wards off the sun's UV rays
So now it's become fashionable, slug cosmetics are all the rage
Do you have to make money from us all the time?
Do you appreciate the poetry of us and our slime?

Chorus

V5
It's hard to be an animal hated by so many humans
With a whole industry devoted to our destruction
The number of slug pellets used here reaches into the billions
But we'd be happy if you'd just leave us some rotting vegetation!

Chorus

Soliloquy of the Slug

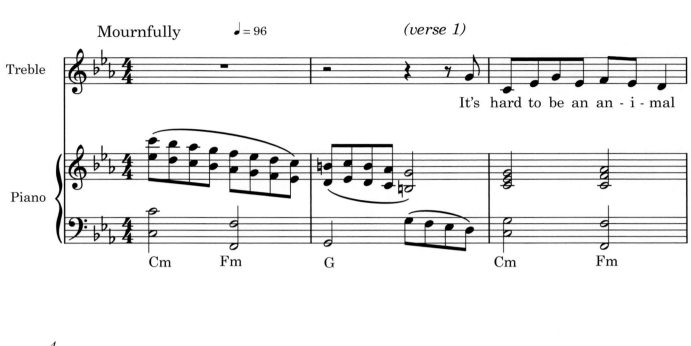

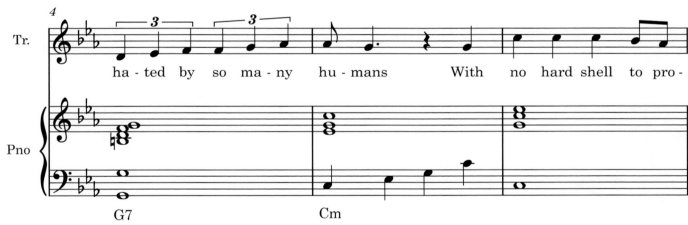

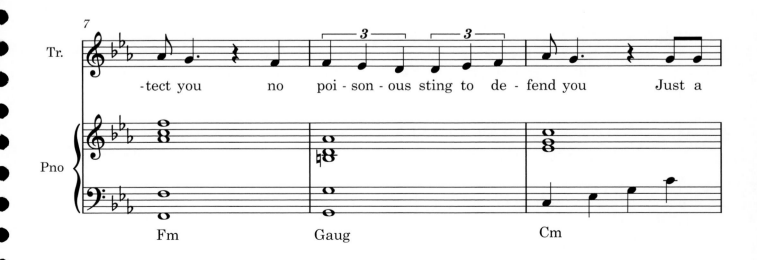

Soliloquy of the Slug

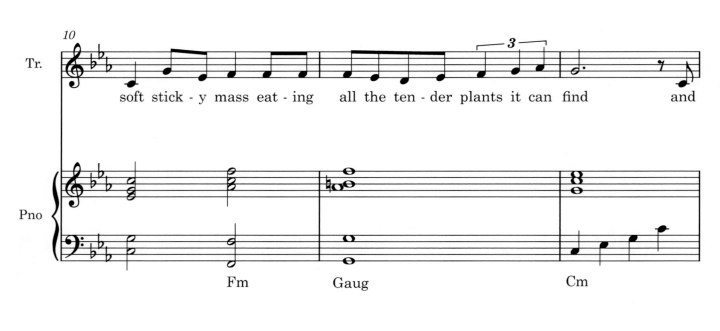

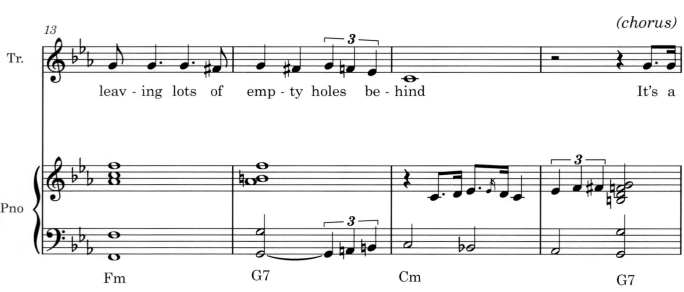

Soliloquy of the Slug

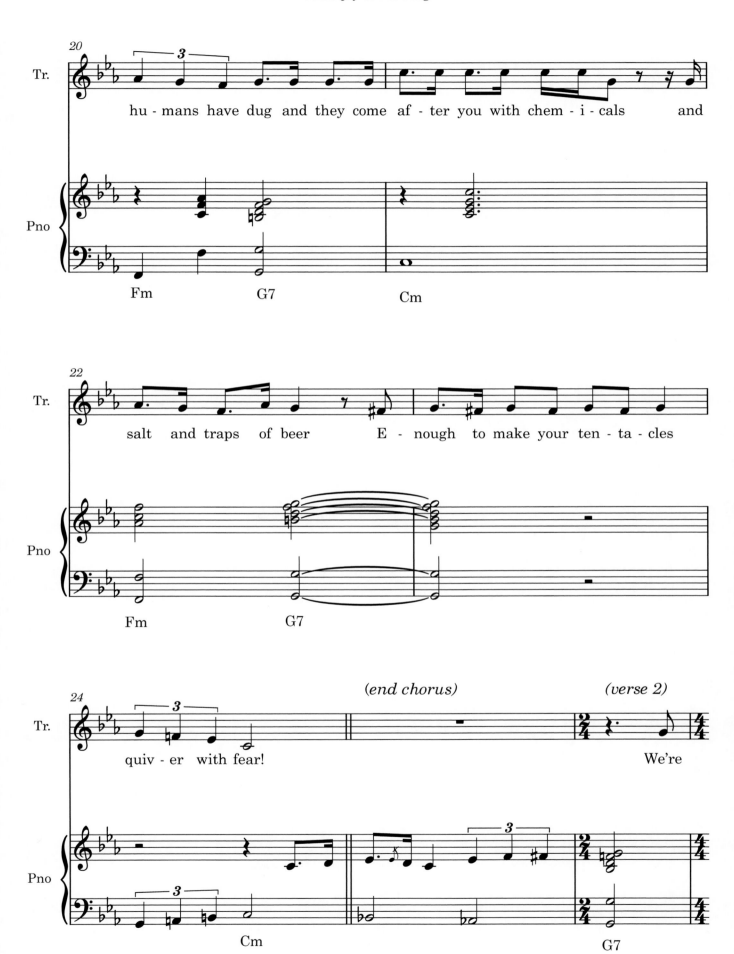

Soliloquy of the Slug

Soliloquy of the Slug

Soliloquy of the Slug

Soliloquy of the Slug

(chorus)

slime o - ver night and day.   It's a

Cm   G7

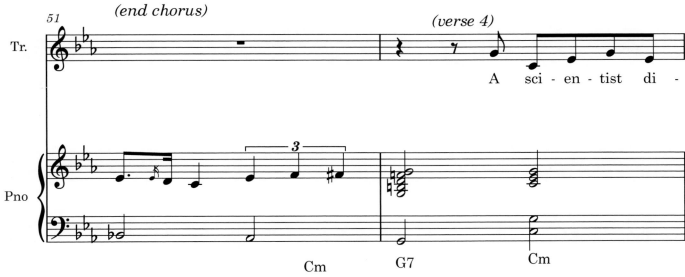

(end chorus)   (verse 4)

A sci - en - tist di -

Cm   G7   Cm

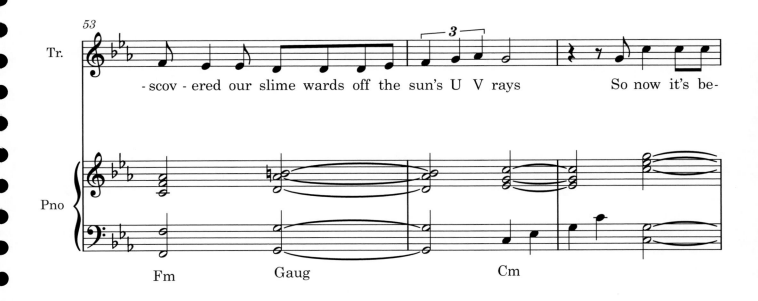

-scov - ered our slime wards off the sun's U V rays   So now it's be-

Fm   Gaug   Cm

Soliloquy of the Slug

Soliloquy of the Slug

168

Soliloquy of the Slug

Soliloquy of the Slug

be a slug when your home's on land that

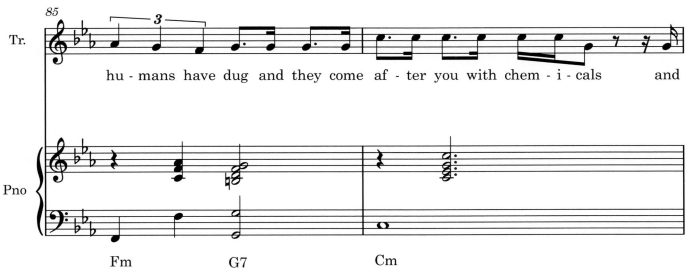

hu - mans have dug and they come af - ter you with chem - i - cals and

salt and traps of beer E - nough to make your ten - ta - cles

Soliloquy of the Slug

quiv - er with fear!

G7   Cm

Life is all around us

In hot tropical areas it's hard not to notice insects and other small creatures, but in, for example, a European winter they may not be so obvious. But when you think that dragon flies may stay under water as nymphs, for months or years, or that bumble bees hibernate in holes, or that earthworms just keep working away underground, or woodworms in old rotten tree trunks, you realise there's always much more going on than you might think.

And there are plenty of creatures in cities too – for example, a certain species of mosquito inhabits the London Underground, and plagued defenceless residents sheltering there from bombs during the Blitz.

It's easy to miss things when you're as big and noisy as a human, particularly if you are in a built up area. But just because we don't notice the rest of life it doesn't mean it's not there, even below pavements and busy roads.

Life is all around us

Chorus:
Life is all around us, in earth, air and water,
Life is all around us, so mind how you go!

V1
Tiny ants are scurrying, building and tunnelling
Spiders are spinning webs between the trees
Wasps and bees will make their nests in cracks, holes and crevices
Bumble queens deep in dreams sleep the winter through

Chorus

V2
Larvae of every kind in rivers and underground
Are growing and changing before they emerge
Earth worms are turning the soil right beneath your feet,
Moths may be dozing under stalks and leaves

Chorus

V3
Earwigs are nestling, tucked into fruit and flowers
Grasshoppers wait for warm summer days
Woodlice are curled up in compost and under bark
Flies search for sunshine to warm up their wings

Chorus

V4
Snails cluster closely in damp nooks and crannies.
Centipedes whizz at speed through the garden soil
Silverfish may fall in love just inside your cupboards
Underneath the floorboards, there may be open war!

Chorus

V5
No matter what the weather, the season or time of day
Life is all around us, wherever we go
Myriads of creatures, of all shapes and sizes
Though we may not see or hear them - life goes on!

Chorus

Life is all around us

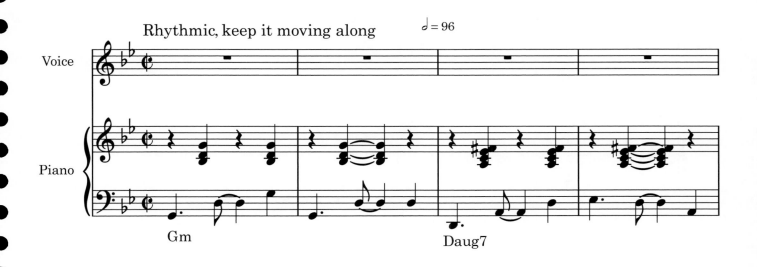

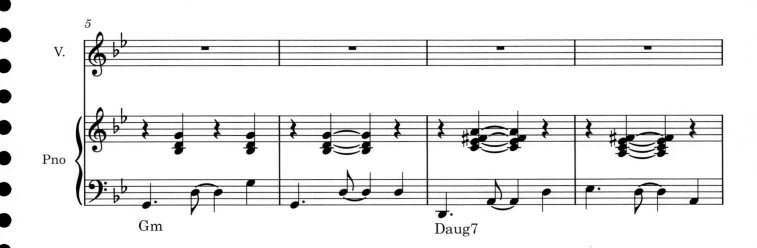

Life is all around us

Life is all around us

Life is all around us

Life is all around us

Life is all around us

Life is all around us

Life is all around us

Life is all around us

all shapes and si - zes   Though we may not see or hear them

Cm

Gm

(chorus) (ends) **rit.**

life goes on!   mind

G♯/D   Gm   Daug7   G♯/D

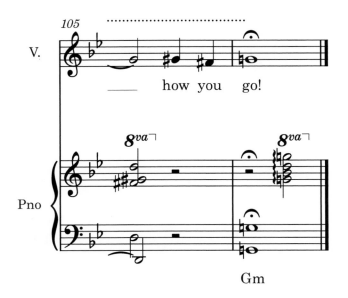

how you go!

Gm